CW00550351

The Science of Microdosing Psychedelics

Torsten Passie

Preface by David Nichols PhD

First published by
Psychedelic Press
London, UK

Copyright © 2019
Torsten Passie and Psychedelic Press

ISBN: 978-0992808884

Editor: **Rob Dickins**
Copy-editing and graphs: **Nikki Wyrd**
Graphs, design and typesetting: **Peter Sjöstedt-H**

Cover photo: LSD crystals
Originally printed in the United Kingdom

For more information:
www.psychedelicpress.co.uk

Those who try to comprehend a phenomenon like LSD must guard against the acceptance of over-simple explanations.

– Louise Richards, Milton Joffe & George Spratto, 1969

Acknowledgements

Many thanks to Professor David Nichols PhD and James Fadiman PhD for reviewing and revising main parts of the manuscript.

Essential help and revisions in respect to issues of pharmacology and tolerance research came from Professor Matthias Liechti MD (University of Basel, Switzerland) and Tobias Buchborn PhD (Imperial College, London).

I am especially thankful to my editor Nikki Wyrd, who did considerable work to make this book free of language errors and hopefully a pleasure to read. Many thanks to Peter Sjöstedt-H for the cover graphics, typesetting and design; and to the publisher, namely Robert Dickins, with whom it was a pleasure to work.

Contents

All doses as given in this booklet are taken per mouth if not stated otherwise.

One milligram (mg) is one thousandth of a gram, one microgram (µg) is one thousandth of a milligram, e.g. 100 µg is one tenth of a milligram.

Preface

— David Nichols —

L et me start by saying that this book contains summaries and analyses of all the published scientific studies of LSD in humans that have been conducted with low doses of LSD; in the range of 5–50 μg. According to one of the more common definitions, microdoses of LSD (or other psychedelics like psilocybin or mescaline) are doses that are one tenth (or less) of a usual dose. Microdoses, strictly speaking, are therefore well below the threshold for producing the characteristic psychoactive effects of psychedelics experienced at higher dosages. It is an astonishing fact that despite all the hype about microdosing in recent years and an obvious thirst for knowledge about its potential effects, nobody has carried out a systematic search of the scientific literature on the use of low doses of psychedelics. This gap in knowledge is filled by Dr Torsten Passie's book.

In the last year I have received numerous requests for interviews about microdosing. What is it? Does it work? How does it work? In each case, I told the interviewer that in the absence of a randomized placebo-controlled clinical trial (RCT) there is no real evidence that microdosing has any demonstrable benefits. This void in our knowledge is unlikely to be filled any time soon because of the very high cost of an RCT of sufficient size. In virtually all documented cases, we also lack knowledge about the actual identity or dosage of drug that people who microdose are using.

Yet, we hear claims from people who are microdosing, particularly LSD, saying it has improved their lives in some way. From a scientific perspective it makes no difference how many people make such claims, because their reports are *anecdotal evidence*, which is much like gossip; it spreads quickly, but is often unreliable. What most people fail to grasp is the power of the placebo effect. A placebo is a substance that has no physiological effect; it is an inert substance. If you give someone suffering from pain a sugar pill and tell them it is a new painkiller, a significant percentage of them will say that they received pain relief; this is the power of suggestion. Mind over matter is a very powerful concept that is often underappreciated. If you hear that Silicon Valley engineers are taking microdoses of LSD to enhance their creativity, your curiosity is naturally raised. If you can obtain microdoses of LSD, and try them, you have an expectancy that you too will experience enhanced creativity, or focus, or whatever. After all, if Silicon Valley geniuses say it works, they must be correct. Right? Likewise, Internet surveys of microdosers will not create a scientific basis for microdosing, they simply represent a collection of anecdotal reports, and if they are positive they will reinforce the suggestion that microdosing actually works in everyone. Placebos can have apparent beneficial effects in any type of physical or mental ailment but are especially powerful when directed toward targets in the brain.

Pharmacologists examine the effects of drugs using a dose-response function. It is generally represented as an S-shaped curve, with drug dose on the x-axis, and function on the y-axis. At low doses, at the bottom of the curve, the effect is absent or minimal, whereas when the dose is increased the action of the drug gradually becomes evident until it reaches some maximum effect. With respect to LSD, other than a few studies hinting that LSD might enhance creativity at higher doses (e.g. 100 μg), there is no scientific evidence that even these high doses of LSD actually enhance creativity or improve cognition. How then, from a purely scientific pharmacological perspective, could a dose only one-tenth as large have such effects?

That is not to say that a microdose of LSD is completely without any effect. In Chapters 6 and 8, we read of a study by Greiner and co-workers in 1958, who reported changes in galvanic skin responses after doses of 5 µg LSD, and pupil size alterations with 10 µg. According to this study, which has some methodological shortcomings, some subjects felt effects at doses as low as 7 or 12 μg. Admittedly, there may be some individuals who are exquisitely sensitive to the effects of LSD, but they will be exceptions to the rule. One is led to infer that perhaps some, but not all, persons might experience effects of a microdose.

What is crucial at the present time is a critical presentation of the known facts, their interrelatedness with other data about the properties of the substances and their interactions with the human organism (tolerance development, potential adverse effects etc.). Therefore we owe thanks to the author (and some leading scientists in the field, who have reviewed parts of the manuscript) for this meticulous presentation, contextualization and interpretation of the data known at present. With this book, the reader has the information at hand needed to make his or her own judgement of the facts, possibilities and potentials of microdosing, as well as the use of low doses of LSD and other psychedelics. I invite you to read the review presented in this book and see for yourself what is known about the effects of microdosing and low-dose LSD. I also eagerly await results from several proposed randomized placebo-controlled studies of microdose LSD.

David Nichols PhD

September 2018, Chapel Hill, NC

1

Introduction

Psychedelic drugs have been a major area of interest in science ever since the discovery of LSD's psychoactive effects in 1943, which in turn promoted the discovery of the brain's neurotransmitter systems. LSD experiences also provided insights into the subjective experiences of psychotic patients and for some time this drug was thought to be the key to revealing the mechanisms of many psychiatric illnesses (Ulrich & Patten 1991, Dyck 2005). Since the mid-1950s, LSD's effectiveness for intensifying psychotherapy was researched on an international scale (Abramson 1967). In the mid-1960s, lay experimentation began, which escalated in the latter part of the 1960s (cf. Lee & Shlain 1985). Despite the fact that no significant problems resulted from either scientific research or therapeutic use (Cohen 1960, Malleson 1973), research projects using psychedelics decreased from a few hundred in the mid-1960s to very few in the 1970s, and virtually nothing in the 1980s and 1990s. However, the Swiss Academy of Medical Sciences was less hostile than the default international position, and organized a first-class scientific symposium entitled "50 years of LSD" in 1993 (Pletscher & Ladewig 1994).

A recent revival of psychedelic research

It took more than 15 years from that Swiss symposium in 1993 until the revival of broader research with psychedelic drugs began in earnest; referred to by some as the renaissance of psychedelics in psychiatry (Sessa 2017). At a lot of major American and European universities, scientific research with LSD and other psychedelics has now been firmly established (cf. Liechti 2017).

There are a few reasons for this revival. One of the more important, in my opinion, is the recently declared "crisis of psychopharmacology". Over the last ten years it became obvious that most conventional psychopharmacological agents were validated by highly biased research. The efficacy of so-called "antidepressant drugs" is especially in doubt. As studies and meta-analyses have shown, these drugs are nearly ineffective in treating many types of depression. It appears that effects on the target symptoms are so small, that it was argued that their differences compared to placebo are "clinically insignificant" (e.g. Kirsch et al. 2008). In other words, the differences to placebo are so small that experienced raters are unable to distinguish them. Evidence of this has been recently recognized in the medical community (Moncrieff 2007).

As a result of this "crisis of psychopharmacology", the pharmaceutical industry has deserted research into novel psychopharmacological agents for nearly ten years. It can be assumed that the industry well knows about problems with their studies, resulting in the "hopeless" psychopharmacology of today. As a side-effect, much less funding has been provided by the industry for academic psychopharmacology since 2010, a fact which has indirectly contributed to the revival of research with psychedelics. Scientific research with psychedelics, including virtually all the major clinical studies, has been funded during the last 25 years mostly by private or non-profit sponsors.

Recent results produced by these studies in patient populations were so profound that one can foresee a revival of therapy with psychedelic drugs (Rucker et al. 2017). Psilocybin and MDMA are actually in the process of conventional medication development processes with both the US Federal Drug Administration (FDA) and the European Medicines Agency (EMA). Clinical studies with psilocybin-assisted psychotherapy for depression, and in patients with anxiety associated with a life-threatening disease, as well as MDMA-assisted psychotherapy for Post-Traumatic Stress Disorder (PTSD) have actually reached Phase 3, the last phase of clinical tests before marketing approval.

The number of people taking LSD recreationally has not declined much since the 1970s (Henderson & Glass 1994, SAMSHA 2016). When MDMA became popular as a dance drug on an international scale in the early 1990s, LSD use also increased. This time, not for inducing psychedelic mystical experiences, but rather as a stimulant drug, with lower doses (50–100 µg), often taken together with MDMA (called 'candyflipping'). In the early 2000s a decline of recreational LSD use was recorded, caused by busts of major illegal LSD producers (Grim 2004). It is assumed that production has recovered since 2010.

Microdosing as a tool in pharmacology

Standard methods of investigating the safety and efficacy of a potential human medicine involve many laboratory animals, sometimes with considerable suffering. Since 1994, researchers evaluated how humans could participate safely in biomedical studies to replace laboratory animal testing. Meanwhile, European legislation requires that Replacement, Reduction, and Refinement (the three Rs) of animal procedures are implemented wherever possible (Combes et al. 2003, EMA 2004).

In pharmacology, microdosing refers to the administration of a substance to humans in miniscule doses, below the threshold for any overt pharmacological activity. Recent progress in the sensitivity of analytic and imaging methods allows the detection of tiny amounts of substances and their activity in the human organism. It is also possible to label a molecule radioactively and then look for its fate in the organism (Tewari & Mukherjee 2010). Such "pre-Phase I studies" can be used to screen drug candidates at an early stage of development to save costs, time and effort. Medical authorities as the EMA and the FDA have adopted the concept and legitimacy of such studies since 2004. A while ago, the EMA recommended such studies to eliminate drug candidates that show sub-optimal human pharmacokinetics (EMEA 2004).

According to published guidelines, a microdose is described as 1/100th of the expected pharmacologically effective dose. With the use of these tiny doses, preclinical toxicology tests required are minimal, although some limited animal tests would still be necessary to check for the toxicological risks of novel chemicals.

The question arises as to whether the results from a microdosing study can predict results of a full-dose pharmacokinetic study. This is by no means a certainty. Various practical issues can vitiate results, but recent studies show that microdosing can be used as a valid tool for predicting pharmacokinetics and metabolism in humans (Lappin et al. 2006). 80% of drugs tested by the oral route (and 100% by the intravenous route) have exhibited scalable pharmacokinetics between a microdose and a therapeutic dose. Compared with other predictive pharmacokinetic methods such as physiologically based pharmacokinetic modelling, allometry, and in vitro-in vivo extrapolation, microdosing appears to provide a significantly better understanding of pharmacokinetics prior to the use of larger doses in humans (Lappin 2015).

Microdosing fertilizers as a new agricultural technology

"Microdosing" is a term used beyond pharmacology. One area it promises to positively affect is the land degradation that affects more than half of the African continent, leading to decreased crops and widespread hunger. To address the problem of soil fertility, which is a greater constraint to food production than drought across much of sub-Saharan Africa, scientists at the International Crops Research Institute for the Semi-Arid Tropics (ICRISAT), a non-profit organization that conducts agricultural research in the drylands of Asia and Africa, have developed a new farming technique called 'microdosing'. Microdosing fertilizers involves the application of very small quantities of fertilizer with the seed at planting time, or as top dressing 3 to 4 weeks after emergence, instead of spreading fertilizer over the entire field (Camara et al. 2013).

This technique uses only about 1/10th of the amount of fertilizer typically used on wheat, and 1/20th of the amount used on corn in the USA. By correcting soil deficiencies for essential nutrients with tiny doses, root systems develop and capture more water, increasing yields. Studies have shown that this method enhances fertilizer use efficiency and can more than double crop yields (Tovihoudii et al. 2017). The technique of microdosing fertilizers takes effort and is time-consuming, but has been envisioned to have the potential to end widespread hunger in drought-prone areas of Africa (International Crops Research Institute for the Semi-Arid Tropics 2009, 2011).

The recent history of microdosing with psychedelics

In the years following 2010, the idea of taking low doses, or microdoses, of LSD became popular. The idea of taking low doses of LSD is not new, but it has emerged again recently, notably in James Fadiman's book (2011), which contains a chapter on the effects of very small ("sub-perceptual") doses of LSD. During his research Fadiman began to use the term "microdosing" when referring to low doses of LSD. Interest in microdosing was boosted when Fadiman was interviewed by Tim Ferriss in March 2015. Shortly after the podcast was aired, an article on microdosing appeared in *Rolling Stone* magazine. Journalists picked up on the "new trend" and began to write articles, which boosted awareness and interest.

At first, it was reported that microdosing was limited to some creative workaholics in Silicon Valley, but after a few more articles appeared, its popularity spread significantly. In a recent book, popular author Ayelet Waldman claimed that microdosing helped to save, or had improved, her mood, life, and marriage (Waldman 2017). However, her book does not contain real evidence that microdosing has done what she claimed it had. She claims to be a highly labile person who has been "held hostage by the vagaries of mood" (Waldman, quoted in Khazan 2017) and may be not the ideal person to register the subtle changes claimed for microdosing. Fadiman's survey on self-reported effects of microdosing provides a more systematic approach (Fadiman & Korb 2017).

Why microdosing became popular

A Reddit forum dedicated to microdosing has grown its subscribers base from 1,600 at the start of 2015 to almost 7,500 in June 2016, and by June 2018 had grown to 31,000.

Interest was prompted by some Silicon Valley executives and engineers who began to microdose for better work performance. These early pioneers, it appears now, have caused microdosing to become a performance-enhancing mini-trend in the computer-tech world, though no numbers are known of those people involved with microdosing. Some think thousands, others place the figure in the hundreds. It seems that it started within some hard-working Silicon Valley circles as part of their usual "perform better" culture. One writer characterized the typical microdoser as "an 'übersmart twentysomething' curious to see whether microdosing will help him or her work through technical problems and become more innovative". (Leonard 2015).

Some of these people, searching for creative and money-making solutions, report success with low doses of LSD at work. They describe enhanced mental flexibility, more focus, more lateral and unconventional thinking. It appears to fit into their quest to work harder, faster, longer. These people are known for their will to try everything to push their performance, even if the strategy is recognized as risky. Typical statements by microdose aficionados go like this: "Microdosing has helped me come up with some new designs to explore and new ways of thinking" (Leonard 2015) or "it helps me think more creatively and stay focused. I manage my stress with ease and am able to keep my perspective healthy in a way that I was unable to before" (Bewellbuzz 2016).

It is well known that every few years there is a new trend that sweeps through the high-tech areas of the US, and claims for enhanced mental powers make the rounds (Repantis et al. 2010), but that its distribution and effects might be overestimated (Partridge et al. 2011). Epidemiological studies show that the Bay Area has had issues related to the use/abuse in the workplace of stimulants like Adderall (amphetamine), Provigil (modafinil) and Ritalin (methylphenidate). Molly Maloof, a physician of the San Francisco Bay Area, sees a "drug problem" and recommends more prosaic remedies instead, which work pretty well: sleep well, get exercise, eat healthy food, and do some meditation or yoga. But "most people are not doing all the basic stuff, and they're taking pills to try to get there. Everyone wants a shortcut" (Maloof, quoted in Cruz 2016: 50). Another factor in favour of microdosing may be that microdosers will not suffer any problematic or even traumatic psychological experiences from their use of psychedelics. Nevertheless, they should be aware that both microdosing and (especially) minidosing can compromise their everyday performance, e.g. handling complex machinery.

Opponents of microdosing

Academic researchers have doubted the effects of microdosing and have warned about the unknown long-term effects of regular intake of psychedelics such as LSD, e.g. Nichols (2017). Some proponents of the use of psychedelics for "consciousness-expansion" and mystical experiences have argued that the "sacred psychedelics" will be robbed of their religious and subversive potential by being "abused" in low doses for utilitarian performance-enhancing purposes. Others have suggested that the subversive potential of LSD is lost in dose ranges that do not allow for any "deconditioning", "psychedelic" or "mystical" experience. One such opponent wrote to a microdosing advocate:

> *By using high doses of LSD, I seriously risked both my freedom and my sanity in an attempt to make the world a better place. Now you are trying to tell me some horseshit about how people should do the opposite and strengthen their egos and ingrain their prejudices by using microdose LSD? (Anonymous 2018)*

Filmmaker and writer Douglas Rushkoff has claimed that "LSD became Prozac [an SSRI antidepressant]. A chemical, which was endangering societal order, became a technology for social control" (Rushkoff 2018).

Booklets and a book on microdosing

Since the hype on microdosing began in 2015, a few booklets on the topic have been issued. The booklet by Cruz (2016), who suggests he is a medical doctor, is a potpourri of material which the author has downloaded from the internet, but he does not reference it as such, implying that he has written it all. Contained is some interesting material written by others, but without reference to any scientific studies. Two booklets by Kumar (2016) and Cahal (2016) differ in respect to author's name, title, cover and typesetting, but contain exactly the same text! They give a superficial and optimistic outline of possible effects of microdosing, with no reference to any scientific research. The small book by Luft (2017) is not about microdosing and its effects. It mainly provides an outline of how to purchase LSD and to prepare a solution from LSD blotters to provide "appropriate dosing". The book by Austin (2018), a known proponent of microdosing, contains a lot of claims about microdosing. The main parts of the present book actually deal with psychedelic research using higher doses. The author's scientific background is obviously limited. It has reference sections for each chapter, but no low-dose studies from the past are mentioned.

Three purposes of microdosing

Three types of justification for microdosing psychedelics can be identified. The first and foremost is better performance, to allow more creative thinking, to help focus and open the mind to new and unconventional solutions. The second is to relieve pathological conditions such as anxiety and depression. The third is to help people to come off other psychopharmaceuticals, a process that has been claimed to be considerably eased by microdosing.

Why I have written this book

When James Fadiman started his research on microdosing, we considered cooperating, but I decided that for me, the project was somewhat vague. My interest in the subject was reignited when I came across a 1959 letter from two doctors of the German section of the Swiss pharmaceutical company Sandoz—where LSD had been discovered—to Professor Hanscarl Leuner, a German LSD expert. These doctors reported successful trials, using very low doses of psilocybin, in patients with psychosomatic disorders. When I dug deeper, I came across a lot of studies conducted with very low doses of LSD in the 1950s and 1960s. These studies were undertaken for different purposes, including the treatment of depression. No recent publication or writing on microdosing has mentioned even one these studies. This is an astonishing omission, given the thirst for knowledge on microdosing. This book is intended to present some history, as well as details of the scientific research and evaluations on the subject, in order to further a realistic view.

2

Definitions of
Microdosing and Minidosing

When it comes to less than intense doses of LSD (or some other psychedelics), conventional research has described these as "low doses" or "very low doses". In the recent literature and internet blogs on microdosing, some new terms were created. Fadiman proposed the term "microdosing" (which is a technical term in pharmacology, cf. Introduction). Fadiman, coming from the term "low doses", has progressed via the terminology "sub-perceptual" doses, which refers to a dose which does not give the individual any detectable effect (e.g. 10 µg of LSD), to the terms "sub-dose" and "microdose" and recently "tenner" (i.e. 10 µg of LSD) (Fadiman 2011: 198). According to Fadiman a sub-perceptual dose of a psychedelic is usually "one-tenth" of a usual dose, which would imply with LSD a dose of 10–25 µg, if a usual dose is considered 100–250 µg. In past research, by far the most common doses given were either 1 µg per kg body weight, or a dose of 100 µg per individual subject (cf. Hollister 1967, Leuner 1962, Hintzen and Passie 2010). Different terms have been used to describe the use of low doses of LSD (Table 1).

Non-hallucinogenic doses	Sicuteri 1977
Sub-perceptual doses	Fadiman 2011
Sub-hallucinogenic doses	Fanciullacci et al. 1974
Sub-tripping doses	Trout 2017
Low-dose LSD	Greiner et al. 1958
Microdosing	Fadiman 2011
Milddosing	Fadiman 2011
Minidosing	Passie 2018, Austin 2018

Table 1: Terms that have been used when referring to dosing with low-dose LSD

In the available literature, two different definitions of microdosing exist:

1. Taking a dose without a detectable acute effect (5–<20 µg LSD)

This definition is consistent with what Fadiman's first subjects told him about microdosing: take 1/20th to 1/10th of a recreational dose of LSD and "stick with your normal patterns, especially eating, working, and sleeping. … Take a micro-dose one day, then carefully observe any ongoing or lingering effects the second day, and then give the third day completely off" (Charles, in: Fadiman 2015: 199–200). "Sub-doses of 10 to 20 micrograms allow me to increase my focus, open my heart, and achieve breakthrough results while remaining integrated within my routine, [and] I am fully able to navigate all manner of logistics and social interactions. … If you are experiencing visual effects, you have taken too much" (Madeleine, in: Fadiman 2015: 203). If one follows Fadiman's recommendation, one should take a microdose once every three days and continue the microdosing for several weeks. Follow your usual routine while microdosing. Take notes throughout the entire process on both short-term, in-the-moment effects, and long-term changes in your mood, energy, and social behaviour.

Fadiman (2018) has clearly stated that "any dose that has, as determined by the person taking it, any psychedelic affects, either perceptual or cognitive, that dose is too high and is not an actual microdose".

It has been scientifically demonstrated that normal subjects cannot reliably detect any effects at the 10–20 µg dose range, but pupil size and galvanic skin response are both altered at 7 µg (cf. Greiner et al. 1958). However, the descriptions as given (Greiner et al. 1958: 209) suggest that their subjects felt some subjective effects even with doses as low as 7 and 12 µg (cf. Chapter 7.1). Nevertheless, the consensus in the scientific literature suggests a threshold dose of 20 µg LSD for detectable subjective effects.

2. Taking a low dose of a psychedelic with some detectable effects ("minidosing")

An example of this would be a 25–50 µg dose of LSD. In this dose range, for most individuals, effects on perception, cognition and ego-functioning are observed. Effects of LSD in this dose range are usually identifiable by outside observers (e.g. Hewitt 1960). It is also clear that some psychological and neurocognitive effects result from these doses, which are felt as "distracting" for everyday performance by most individuals. To some therapists and researchers these doses seemed useful because they "activate" the psyche. Low doses enhance sensitivity, the perception of emotions, and might provoke memories and catharsis. It has been argued that in this "psycholytic" dose range an "ego-enhancement" (Abramson) takes place, which helps integrate unconscious material. Most neuropsychological tests do not show deficits in performance at this dose range, although some do. An example of this definition of microdosing is by Cruz (2016), who reports that "objects seem to glow", a warped sense of time, enhanced sense of touch, smell and hearing and "sometimes synaesthesia", which are all phenomena that appear with doses higher than 20 µg. Austin (2018: 123) gives the following definition: of a minidose: "… a dose strong enough that it is no longer truly sub-perceptual … . Minidosing can be tremendously impactful for ideation and improving abstract reasoning while still leaving you with enough control to not only fully function in normal circumstances but also to assimilate your divergent thinking into a plan of action" (Austin 2018: 123).

In this book, I shall use the term "minidosing" for the use of doses of LSD slightly above the perceptual threshold (25–50 µg). Diagram 1 provides an overview of the different doses as used with microdosing and minidosing and some claimed effects.

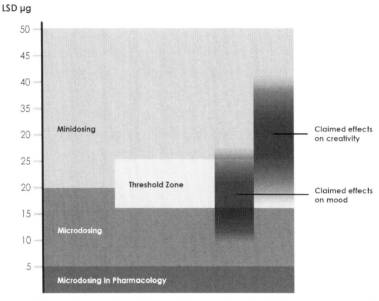

Diagram 1: Schematic overview of different dose levels with minidosing and microdosing and some claimed effects

The frequency of intake with micro- or minidosing depends on the purpose. In some descriptions or definitions, a pattern of daily intake is implied. "Fadiman's protocol" recommends taking a dose of 10–20 µg every third day. Empirical data from Fadiman and Korb shows, however, that in their surveys most people tend to micro- or minidose erratically. Only a few (<5%) do it on a regular basis for a few intakes, but usually not for more than two weeks. No more than three people (out of nearly two thousand) in their survey have done it for 90 days or more (Korb 2018b).

It is noteworthy that the "protocols" given by Fadiman (2011) for microdosing have an unusual pattern of drug intake, which deviates from conventional medications. With usual medications, the ingestion is done when a certain symptom appears (e.g. pain, low blood sugar in diabetes, etc.) or is taken long-term, usually on a daily basis (e.g. to treat high blood pressure). There is no known medication that is usually taken in this kind of pattern, a uniqueness amplified by the fact that it is a substance with a half-life of a few hours and is out of the system after dosing in less than a day or two.

Knowing the dose

It has repeatedly been stated that it's hard to know the identity of the drug which has been taken by microdosers, when the drug comes from illegal sources. Even if the identity of the drug is known, the user is left with the question of how very low doses can be accurately known when an illegal LSD preparation has been purchased. In respect to knowing the dose, there are two current approaches: From 2012 on, drug suppliers on the Dark Web and from other sources began offering microdoses on tabs. Each tab claimed to hold 10 µg. The other practice used widely is to take a tab/blotter containing 100 µg (the most usual amount sold) and place it in 100 millilitres of distilled water. One millilitre would then hold 1 µg, making measurements easy. This approach is called "volumetric dosing" (e.g. Austin 2018).

3
The History of Microdosing

If one searches for the use of low doses of LSD or other psychedelics in the vast research literature on these substances, it seems as if there has been no research focused on this regimen. But that isn't true. In the course of much lively and extensive experimentation with LSD, a lot of different dose regimens were used. They included research into the lowest detectable dose of LSD, repeated dosing with low doses, and research into the development of tolerance to LSD, where subjects were given low or high doses daily, for weeks or even months. Most experiments and therapeutic applications used doses of 75–150 µg by mouth. However, some experimenters used much lower doses and others were eager to find out about dose-response by using different doses in the same experiment. Most of those studies were done in the 25–50 µg range, but some used even smaller doses.

This chapter will introduce the reader to the "history" of low-dose LSD by outlining what happened regarding this before the hype about LSD microdosing took off around 2015.

Use of low doses of hallucinogenic plants by indigenous cultures

It has been speculated (Fadiman 2011: 198) that low doses or microdoses may have been used by indigenous cultures or tribes for centuries. Not much is known about this possibility. It is known that some members of the Tarahumara tribe in southern Mexico were anxious about the strong psychological effects of the mescaline-containing peyote cactus (*Lophophora williamsii*) and demonstrated an ambivalent attitude about its stronger effects. Nevertheless, peyote is definitely used as a sacrament in some of their rituals. For the most part, the Tarahumara don't take peyote or other related cacti (e.g. *Ariocarpus fissuratus* and *Mammillaria craigii*) in doses sufficient to cause the strong psychological effects which are usually assumed as standard for the hallucinogens. Anthropologists have documented the use of different psychoactive cacti primarily for increasing endurance, especially for running longer distances or for hunting expeditions (Bye 1979). "The Tarahumara Indians consume small amounts of peyote to combat hunger, thirst, and exhaustion—especially while hunting" (Gottlieb 1997: 14). It appears that they avoid strong hallucinogenic effects by using low doses (Deimel 1980). It may also be true that hallucinogenic plants that also (probably) contain stimulant-like substances are more likely to be used in lower than hallucinogenic doses for their stimulant "strengthening" properties. However, other than this, anthropologists have not reported the usage of low doses of hallucinogenic plants. One can suppose that its marginal distribution, use out of sacred contexts and a lower potential for harm might have made this methodology "invisible".

Ethnopharmacologist and psychedelic researcher Terence McKenna (1992) has proposed that human ancestors who lived in the Sahara desert in Africa used low doses of psilocybin to enhance their perceptual acuity to be better hunters.

Research on "the lowest detectable dose of LSD" (1947–1967)

In the first clinical trial with LSD, psychiatrist Arthur Stoll (1947) gave 20–40 μg to his subjects in a comprehensive observational study. He found 20 μg to be undetectable, whereas 30 μg produced some light symptoms, which peaked two hours later than with 100 μg. Working under contract to the US Air Force, Greiner et al. (1958) found reactions in galvanic skin response with doses of 5 μg LSD, pupil size alterations with 10 μg, and subjective effects felt above 20 μg. Canadian psychiatrist Abram Hoffer's subjects did not detect 15 μg, whereas the majority felt some effects after 25 μg (Hoffer and Osmond 1967). Test subjects of De Maar et al. (1960) received LSD several times and could identify differences between doses of 25, 50, and 100 μg. In another experiment with 50 μg, most subjects reported slight difficulty in focusing vision, inner trembling, dream-like feeling, weakness, heaviness or lightness of limbs, while neuropsychological measures were found to be unaffected (Abramson et al. 1955).

In a research study by McGothlin and Cohen, healthy subjects took 200 µg LSD and the control group got 25 µg as an "active placebo" (McGothlin et al. 1967). At a 1967 conference, LSD researcher Walter Pahnke asked about reactions in the 25 µg group. McGothlin answered: "They are very mild, I'd say. ... We had hoped that our twenty-five µg group would think they had received LSD ... But, in fact, only two [out of 20] of our people who have gotten the low dose have reported that they received LSD. Occasionally, a person will go pretty well, will lie down and report some visual or auditory effect from twenty-five µg, but a good share of them report very little in the way of a reaction ..." (McGothlin 1967: 40).

A German psychotherapist microdosed patients in 1955

Dr Walter Frederking, a German psychiatrist, became interested in the use of drugs in psychoanalytic therapy in 1949. He pioneered the use of mescaline and LSD in psychotherapy. In the usual course of psychoanalytic therapy (with an average of 100–200 sessions), 5–10 drug sessions with 30–60 µg LSD were implemented. According to Frederking, "the procedure is indicated when it is desirable to shorten a course of therapy, reactivate a stalled treatment of a neurosis, and for the purpose of breaking down affect or memory blocks" (Frederking 1955: 265). Frederking also described how his patients reacted to very low doses with "dissolution of cramps and tensions". A man who suffered from intestinal cramps for months became free of this after a single dose of 25 µg. Similarly, Frederking successfully treated trepidations, general cramping or inhibitions, through one or more low doses of LSD (mostly 20–25 µg), which he gave his patients to take at home for a few days in a row. He also reported faster progress in psychotherapy when patients took low doses for a few days. When patients took those at home they felt agreeable bodily sensations like feeling very light for some hours, but in a few cases they saw "dreamlike pictures" for seconds (Frederking 1953/54: 357).

Minidosing LSD to help spiritual exploration

When prominent LSD researcher Sidney Cohen found that "though we have been using the available measuring instruments, the check lists, the performance tests, the psychological batteries, and so forth, the core of the LSD situation remains quite untouched by our activities", he turned to an expatriate writer with spiritual and esoteric knowledge to get more articulate reports of the drug's effects. Gerald Heard immediately became enthusiastic about the mystical aspects of the LSD experience. Later on, Heard recommended the use of low doses of LSD for the enhancement of spiritual practices, such as meditation and prayer (Heard 1959). According to psychedelic expert Metzner (2019), psychologist Wilson van Dusen, who has written about "LSD and the enlightenment of Zen" (1961), has done low-dose LSD experiments for the same purposes.

The same recommendation came later on from Myron Stolaroff, a psychedelic pioneer who undertook research with psychedelics since the early 1960s. He had known dysfunctional effects from taking "half a dose" or less, which usually leads to restlessness and dysphoria. However, Stolaroff was better informed by a psychologist, who impressed him by taking very low doses but having "wonderful experiences". After some similar experiments, Stolaroff concluded that most people avoid taking lower doses because they don't want to get into "uncomfortable feelings". However, he found that these feelings are precisely the ones that interfere with people's lives, and are those that they need resolved. "Therefore it is worthwhile to experience them, confront them, and resolve them" (Stolaroff 1994: 105). In his low-dose experiments, Stolaroff obviously confronted uncomfortable feelings:

> *Most of the time it was a vague, sluggish feeling that I did not specifically recognize. As I held my attention steadily on it, it would become more clear. Often I began to understand what my true feeling was, what were my true desires, or what I was doing wrong with my life or relationships. With recognition, my feelings would begin to release and simply float away ... my feeling of well-being began to rise, as did my energy level.*

He concluded that in many cases he would get experiences from low doses comparable to higher doses. However, he claims that he "resolved a lot of interior debris, so that I felt much more at peace with myself, and the after-effects of the experience stayed with me in a rewarding way for a much longer time" (Stolaroff 1994: 106). "With low doses, by focusing directly on the feelings and staying with them without aversion and without grasping, they will in time dissipate. Resolving one's repressed feelings in this manner clears the inner being, permitting the True Self to manifest more steadily" (Stolaroff 1999: 61). This statement makes obvious why Stolaroff sees psychedelics as potentially helpful within spiritual practices like meditation. However, it is clear from his writings that he did not use sub-perceptual doses. He used doses of 1/3 to 1/5 of a usual dose of several psychedelics, such as LSD, 2C-T7, and others.

Sandoz tested minidosing with psilocybin in 1959

This psychedelic substance psilocybin was isolated from *Psilocybe spp.* mushrooms and was synthesized in 1958 by Swiss chemist Albert Hofmann, the discoverer of LSD, in his lab at the Sandoz pharmaceutical company in Basel, Switzerland. Shortly thereafter, psilocybin was distributed by Sandoz under the trade name Indocybin® to assist psychotherapy.

Until now, there was no evidence that Sandoz ever tested microdosing. This perception changed when I recently browsed through some papers left by the late Professor Hanscarl Leuner (1921–1996), a European pioneer in hallucinogens and psycholytic therapy (cf. Passie 1996/1997). During my search, I came across a letter to Leuner, dated 22 December, 1959. In this letter, two employees from the German Department of the Sandoz Company in Nuremberg (Dr Augsberger and Dr Hammerschmidt) referred to a delivery of psilocybin to Leuner. Mentioning the use of psilocybin in psychotherapy, the doctors report "that relatively high doses of psilocybin are necessary to induce depersonalization phenomena and hallucinations as with LSD". Then they report, "that the administration of 3 mg parenteral or 6 mg per os psilocybin causes a state of euphoric indifference/unconcern. The patient is psychologically and physiologically relaxed and feels himself far away from everyday sorrows. It is this property, which caused us to arrange experimental therapeutic use of psilocybin in some patients with anxiety and obsessional-compulsive symptoms. The doses used with these patients were 2 times 0.5 mg daily to 3 times 2 mg daily. It is too early to definitively judge the efficacy of psilocybin. But at least there have been some quite remarkable successes seen with this treatment" (Augsbrunner and Hammerschmidt 1959, p. 2). It is unknown if these experiments were expanded, but Sercl et al. (1961), who worked in association with Sandoz, did similar experiments in 1960 and reported similar effects from low doses of psilocybin (see Chapter 15).

Microdosing by a psychedelic pioneer in 1960

During the 1950s, Bernard Copley began to take part in Native American peyote rituals. Copley also claimed that he was "fortunate to be accepted by several of our leading psychiatrists as a part of the research programs being conducted to reveal the full possibilities of the hallucinogenic drugs" (Copley 1962: 12). In a brochure on his experiments, he wrote: "I have devoted almost my entire life to the study of the methods by which the consciousness can be expanded into its greatest possible reaches" (Copley 1962: 11). When Copley became acquainted with the synthetic hallucinogens, he tried unusual dosing strategies and conducted "a long series of hallucinogenic tests with emotional direction toward a given thought concept or action" to reach a "constructive purpose". Later on, he wanted,

> *to see how small a dosage of any hallucinogen could be taken without giving too extreme a result. Lysergic acid [=LSD] proved to be merely unpleasant for this use, but mescaline was ideal. For sixty days I took one twentieth of a gram of mescaline at eight o'clock in the morning. On certain days, if I had eaten a little more food than usual or was a little fatigued, I could not tell that I had taken it at all. On other days when the energy cycle was higher than ordinary, or when I ate little or nothing, it almost reached the point where I would not want to carry on daily work or contact with people. The sensation of the small dose is just one of well being.*
> (Copley 1962: 17)

One twentieth of a gram of mescaline is 50 mg, which is 10% of a full oral dose of mescaline, which implies microdosing. Interestingly, Copley didn't experience any tolerance during his 60-day experiment, which might point to a different tolerance pattern with small doses.

Tragically, the 26-year old Copley—together with another early LSD proselyte, Bernard Roseman (1963, 1966)—was charged in 1963 for smuggling LSD into the US. This occurred long before unlicensed use of LSD became illegal in 1966, but they were sentenced for smuggling. Both got 17 years in prison and became the first "LSD martyrs" (Chlodwig 2016).

Low-dose LSD and the US military

The US Army's tests on LSD had many purposes. At first there were tests on the use of drugs like mescaline for forced interrogations, especially of foreign agents (Passie & Benzenhöfer 2018). When LSD appeared on the scene, it was conjectured that with such a substance, which is odourless, tasteless and colourless, it might be possible to spray it over large areas or put in into water supplies of ships or elsewhere. During this research, a lot of CIA-financed studies were conducted on the "prevention" of LSD-intoxication by the use of different substances in advance or during the acute effects of LSD (cf. Sheflin & Opton 1978). To detect how much of the effect of LSD was still detectable it was necessary to know what effects, at which doses, can be seen with LSD. The researchers at Edgewood Arsenal, the Army's centre for chemical warfare, came to the conclusion that, especially in the low-dose range, virtually no serious dose-response studies had been done. The studies conducted on behalf of the US Army at the New York State Psychiatric Institute were inconclusive about the effects of low doses and researchers did not produce differential data with different doses of LSD. They only made general statements such as "below 60 μg ... we found the symptoms produced to be unreliable" (Hoch & Cattell 1952: 581).

For unknown reasons, but presumably for chemical warfare purposes, the US Air Force sponsored a study to objectify subjective and physiological reactions to doses as low as 5 μg (Greiner 1957, Greiner et al. 1958).

A few years later, the US Army initiated a low-dose LSD study on young healthy soldiers to investigate the influence of low doses of LSD on complex intellectual performance. In this study, 100 subjects were tested between 1961 and 1966. Results from the early tests (with doses of 0.5 μg/kg) are unavailable, but some results of a study in 1964 are. This double-blind study used 35 μg LSD against placebo to test chess performance. Subjects were trained in lightning chess before the study began and scores were obtained at hourly intervals. Subjects noted only a slight loss of skill, which was congruent with the objective measures (Ketchum 2006).

A 1980s brand of "Microdose LSD"

In 1980, a new brand of LSD appeared on the drug market in California. Its producers named it; "Clearlight brand 'Microdose' LSD". The first batch was distributed in Berkeley, California in 1980. The tablets each contained 100 milligrams of ascorbic acid and 5 micrograms LSD. They came in brown glass bottles, each containing 100 tablets. These tablets were given away, not sold. In the "Product Information Leaflet" provided with the second batch in 1988 (Figure 1), the producers claim that the LSD was prepared on perforated food-grade sterile paper in the form of tiny machine-cut squares of clear hard gelatine. "During the drying process, various bells and cymbals are used to ecstatically consecrate each batch." 400,000 doses were manufactured, but most of the batch was seized by the DEA around 1992. The insert suggests a use of LSD by "bona-fide healers to catalyze a balanced physical/mental restructuring", for inducing religious experiences and to explore the users' creative potential. Each square of paper contained 5 µg LSD, which "is usually considered to be an extremely low dose". The authors mention that most scientific studies were done with much higher doses, but "some people seem to feel an effect after taking as little as one-quarter ...". Nevertheless, the instructions recommend a dose of 200–400 µg LSD in safe circumstances (Anonymous 2017).

IMPORTANT INFORMATION FOR POTENTIAL USERS OF CLEARLIGHT brand "MICRODOSE" LSD

MANUFACTURE:

Utilizing unique variations of modern homeopathic techniques while working in a dry, dark, low-temperature environment, each of these perforated thin sheets of food-grade sterile paper is evenly saturated with a cold solution containing a highly-refined form of pure pharmaceutical Lysergic Acid Diethylamide (LSD), rapidly cold-dried, and immediately sealed in airtight packages. During the drying process, various bells and cymbals are used to ecstatically consecrate each batch. The result of twenty-five years of intense research, these paper squares contain absolutely no binders, buffers, disintegrants, coatings, lubricants, fillers, colors, inks, dyes, sugars, wheat, corn, gelatin, or artificial flavors.

SUGGESTED USES:

These squares are amazingly versatile psychic tools that have a wide variety of uses. For example, there are numerous ways in which these squares may be employed by a bona-fide healer to catalyze a balanced physical/mental restructuring. Some people consider these squares to be an excellent sacrament if used in an appropriate religious setting. These squares may also prove to be of great value to an intelligent user who is seriously interested in exploring her or his creative potential.

DOSAGE:

Each one-quarter inch by one-quarter inch square of paper contains approximately five micrograms of active LSD. This is usually considered to be an extremely low dose (one microgram is one-millionth of a gram). Many, many, many studies of the effects of LSD have been made by the scientific community. The doses given to people by "legitimate" researchers have ranged from ten micrograms to fifteen-thousand micrograms per dose. The dosage most often mentioned in popular literature is one-hundred micrograms. The first measured dose of LSD taken by a human was two-hundred and fifty micrograms. Quite a few of the people who have made a serious study of the subject think that in some cases the appropriate dose is one that weighs between three-hundred micrograms and five-hundred micrograms. Some people seem to feel an effect after taking as little as one-quarter of a single square of CLEARLIGHT brand "MICRODOSE" LSD.

Figure 1: The above product insert for Clearlight brand "Microdose" LSD was published in the 1980s in Berkeley, California (https://www.flickr.com/photos/jdyf333/2075297284/)

If the story about "Clearlight brand 'microdose' LSD" is true, the origin of the use of the term microdose for very low doses of LSD (as suggested by the 5 µg dose units of this produces) precedes by far all other uses of the term, e.g. in pharmacology (since 1995), in agriculture (since 2005) and by Fadiman (2011).

Recreational microdosing in Peru

Keeper Trout, a researcher best known for his extensive knowledge on psychoactive cacti (e.g. Trout 2005), reported to me at a 2017 conference that in 1981 a friend from Peru had claimed that a common practice among his friends is the peeling of exemplars of the mescaline-containing San Pedro cactus *(Trichocereus pachanoi)* and the sun-drying of thin slices until crispy. His informant claimed that it was a usual practice for them to eat these "like potato chips" before and during soccer matches. "The spectators ate freely to enhance their experience of the game but the players also ate them before the game so they 'could play like tigers'". Trout commented that he had never encountered this story anywhere else, so it might have been limited to just a small group. After he got this information, Trout made a test himself by using small amounts of San Pedro "as a hiking aid" and found it greatly enhanced the experience, but did not give him more energy (like stimulants do). However, "... there was a sense of stimulation but there was also a sense of distraction that balanced or functionally negated it". After a few experiments, Trout found it not useful and did no further experiments (Trout 2018).

Albert Hofmann, discoverer of LSD, and low-dose LSD

It might well be the case that after all the "prehistory" of microdosing as given above, Albert Hofmann himself was a major inspiration of what could be called the "modern era of microdosing". It appears that he has stated consistently to some people that he used low doses of LSD for a while. According to Fadiman, who had not spoken to Hofmann personally, but has interviewed people who had, many claimed that Hofmann took low doses of LSD "for decades" (Fadiman 2011: 54). Fadiman found out about Hofmann's low dose use of LSD through a colleague in California, named Robert Forte, a well-known figure in the psychedelic field (cf. Forte 1997, 1999). According to Forte, Hofmann believed that if Sandoz had been more interested, they might have made low-dose LSD into a product more useful and safer than Ritalin or Adderall. Fadiman, who was informed by Forte about Hofmann's use of low doses of LSD, was under the impression that Hofmann took frequent doses of 10 μg, which might have promoted his good health and longevity. However, recently, Fadiman realized that he was mistaken in this. His informer Forte wrote to the author of the present book:

> *I told Jim that Albert told me he thought it was the most under-researched potential of LSD, that very small doses of LSD could work like an anti-depressant. I certainly did not tell him that Albert did it a lot, ... Who really knows how Albert used LSD? I get the feeling from talking with good friends of his, he didn't use small doses very often ...*
> (Forte 2018)

In a 1976 interview with psychedelic activist and archivist Michael Horowitz for the underground magazine *High Times*, Hofmann reported he had taken LSD about 15 times, the last time in 1970. When Horowitz asked: "What general medical uses might LSD be marketed for in the future?" Hofmann answered: "Very small doses, perhaps 25 micrograms, could be useful as a euphoriant or antidepressant" (Hofmann & Horowitz 1976).

According to Ayelet Waldman, author and microdose enthusiast, Hofmann had also informed psychedelic ethnobotanist Terence McKenna of his regular low-dose experiments, and recommended them for "walking among tall trees" (Waldman 2017: 106). This is congruent with what I personally heard from Hofmann when we sat for breakfast at a 1989 conference in Freiburg/Breisgau, located at the edge of the German Black Forest. Hofmann told me that one should use low doses of LSD "to walk in the forest and observe your thoughts". However, his statement implied a dose above the detectable level. Additional information came from Dr John Halpern, a former assistant professor of psychiatry at the Harvard Medical School, who stated in a recent interview:

> *Once when I had lunch with Albert Hofmann ... about 20 years ago I had asked him about micro-dosing. We had a lively discussion that LSD could have become the first "Prozac"-like antidepressant and that 25*

micrograms a day seemed to be particularly effective. Dr Hofmann stated that he really pushed to make LSD into an antidepressant and had the idea to combine it with an emetic (a drug that would induce vomiting) if too many pills were taken at once. He said that company lawyers thought there were too many risks/pitfalls to offering a drug in such a preparation and so it never was developed for commercial use.
(Horgan & Halpern 2017)

Hofmann himself never published anything (or initiated research) on such low doses beyond his personal experiments. Recently however, historian Mike Jay (2018) discovered and reported a series of low-dose trips that Hofmann undertook between 1943 and 1946, about which he never wrote. During Hofmann's military service in 1943, he took 20 μg LSD at his barracks, on 29th September. As the effects manifested, he reported that "I withdrew almost completely into myself, my own thoughts". He went to bed with images playing across his closed eyes, accompanied by "warm comfortable feelings." A second experiment, on 2nd October, with 20 μg was far less pleasant: "I had disturbing dreams", including "a crazy mutilated woman with her arms cut off and burned out eyes". In a subsequent experiment, on Halloween, Hofmann took 30 μg and felt a "slight daze, shivers, nausea, a faint metallic taste in my mouth", along with some "stimulation in the genital region". He entered "a dozy state", in which "disturbing, uncanny phantasms, partly sensual visions" flitted through his mind. On 17th January, 1946, he took another 30 μg at home. He "was struck by the beautiful colors of the tabletop ... wonderful warm tones that changed from orange to blood-red to purple" (Jay 2018). These reports show that Hofmann had gained experiences with low doses of LSD during the first years following the discovery of LSD. These may have led to the conclusion that LSD might be a useful antidepressant.

In a recent email, a Swiss publisher and close friend of Hofmann, Roger Liggenstorfer, informed me that Hofmann "dosed himself with doses of 30 to 50 μg, sometimes up to 90 μg. He did not dose himself on a regular basis, just rarely" (Liggenstorfer 2018).

Other reports of early microdosing

In the pages of Fadiman's book (2011), a person named Clifford reported that when he was studying biology at University of California at San Diego during the late 1960s, he realized that during a boring biology course "that in order to stay alert, a tiny dose of LSD could be useful. With that in mind, I licked a small, but very potent, tablet … This produced a barely noticeable brightening of colors and created a generalized fascination with the course and my professor, who was otherwise uninteresting to me" (quoted in Fadiman 2011: 206). On the same pages of Fadiman's book, a certain Madeline reported on the results of frequent microdosing for a couple of years. It appears from her report that she began taking low doses of LSD without any knowledge of previous experimentation. She had taken larger doses in the past, but "had never heard of sub-dosing when I began doing it. … I was looking for something to make me feel sparkly and UP at cocktail parties and networking events. … I found that on sub-doses, I made more meaningful and lasting connections, and my own evolution seemed to accelerate ...". One might speculate that she took somewhat higher doses at first, because she reports "success" with her original intention "to feel sparkly and UP". Whatever might be true, she states at the end of her report that "...10 to 20 micrograms of LSD is both a stimulant and a calming agent at the same time" (quoted in Fadiman 2011: 204/5).

Ayelet Waldman, who wrote a book about her four weeks of microdosing, presented a story about an early microdoser. She says that when she gathered information, before starting her experiment, she heard about a professor who had experimented with microdosing for years. She reached out to the professor and was informed that he was nearing the end of his life and was willing to transfer some of the LSD left from his experiments to her. A few days later she found a brown paper package with "a tiny cobalt blue bottle" in her mailbox and started her experiments (Waldman 2017: 7).

Microdosing in recent internet videos

Hupli et al. (2018) have explored "microdosing psychedelics" within YouTube, a video channel on the internet, where people can upload videos. Research on how knowledge on microdosing is created and circulated in social media is thus far non-existent. Initial data extraction resulted in 48 relevant videos. A qualitative analysis was performed on the six most viewed videos, which comprised 92% of the total view counts of all 48 videos (Table 2). The videos tend to revolve around themes like control, research, experiments, self-monitoring, and the imperative of sharing results and relevant information. The authors posit microdosing in the realm of 'pharmacological neuroenhancement', comparable to methylphenidate or some antidepressants (Maier & Schaub 2015).

Video title Date of publication Number of views	Psilocybin mushrooms	LSD	Mescaline
Microdosing LSD or any Psychedelic* September 15, 2015 526,243 views	0.2–0.5 gr. (dried)	10–30 µg	50–75 mg
Mescaline microdose video* Septermber 15, 2015 (?) 148,681 views			80 mg
LSD: microdosing & the supernatural April 23, 2016 108,974 views		10–15 µg	
Microdosing mushrooms: the benefits of microdosing psilocybin!* October 10, 2015 59,255 views	No dose given		
Microdosing psilocybin Mushrooms November 10, 2015 35,928 views	0.2–0.5 gr. (dried)		
'Microdosing' psychedelic drugs has positive effects June 17, 2015 28,167 views	0.2–0.5 gr. (dried)	10–15 µg	50–75 mg

Table 2: Description of the six most viewed YouTube videos on microdosing and dosages recommended (modified from Hupli et al. 2018)
* Indicates that clip is no longer available

The Google-owned YouTube video channel/website has recently deleted videos on microdosing for propagating illegal activity. Since March 2018 video providers have "been targeted" or censored (Hupli 2018).

"Co-tripping" with low doses

One effect known from recreational drug use is that a group consisting of some people on LSD sometimes gives rise to a phenomenon whereby the non-users present might also experience aspects of an altered state of consciousness. The sober person(s) might feel "altered" in some respects, be it in their emotions, mental irritation, laughing about unusual things, and even conceptual cognition. This can happen without any drug whatsoever being taken by those experiencing what is commonly known as a "contact high". Recently I heard about experiences of people who had introduced others to the psychedelic experience by taking LSD with a dose of 100–200 µg LSD. To prevent boredom, whilst at the same time being more sensitive and receptive to the person tripping on a higher dose than a sober state would allow, they took a low dose of around 50 µg. This dose allows for a more empathic response, but retains the ability to perceive and respond without many sensory and cognitive alterations so as to be able to support the other person appropriately and take care of the setting, e.g. environment, music, protection against interferences, eating and drinking. I propose the new term "co-tripping" for this way of using low doses of psychedelics together with others "tripping" on higher doses.

When they started their work with LSD therapy for alcoholics in the mid-1950s, the group around Osmond, Blewett and Hoffer at Regina (Saskatchewan, Canada) tried to take LSD together with their group of patients. When the treatment program became larger, the therapists ran into difficulties with the co-use of the drug in therapeutic sessions by ingesting the drug too often. However, "it has been stated that tolerance for LSD builds up quite rapidly but even when we have run group sessions as frequent as three times a week this has not appeared to be a problem and the therapists have been able to work in close empathy with the subject on doses as low as 25 µg on the third day of such series" (Blewett & Chwelos [1960]: 16).

Soft-trip to treat trauma from preceding use of psychedelics

During the 1994–1996 period, I worked with Professor Hanscarl Leuner, one of the pioneers of hallucinogen research and psycholytic therapy. He had permission to work with LSD, psilocybin and other psychedelics during the 1954–1986 period at his university department at Göttingen University in

Germany (cf. Passie 1997). During my work in his office, we met with a patient who had previously experienced a traumatic psychedelic drug experience. He still felt under the pressure of that experience and had regular intrusive memories related to the event. He came for help and Leuner explained to him that he might be helped by another experience with such a drug. We offered him a session with a low dose of a psychedelic we used at that point in time, a short-acting derivative of mescaline. He was anxious at first, but as he found he could easily control the effects of the low dose he became more and more comfortable with the effects. When he was more able to let go, the traumatic experience came up again and he was able to re-experience it without too much anxiety. When he was back from what Leuner called the "soft-trip", he was able to handle his memories with greater ease and was healed from the trauma in the long run. This case is just a single report and limitations are obvious. Nevertheless, it is possible that this soft-trip regimen could be helpful with the treatment of traumatic after-effects of psychedelic use in some cases.

4

The Research of James Fadiman

Dr James "Jim" Fadiman, an American psychologist, has been involved with the study of psychedelics since the early 1960s. He is known for his early research on the therapeutic effects of psychedelic therapy (Fadiman, 1965) at The International Foundation for Advanced Study, in Menlo Park, California. He was also part of the team that conducted a study into the possible creativity-enhancing effects of moderate doses of psychedelics (Harman and Fadiman, 1970). When unlicensed use of LSD became illegal, he made a career as a management consultant and cofounded the Institute for Transpersonal Psychology, in Palo Alto California. He was, and still is, invited to report on his early LSD research on some occasions, but is not part of the "psychonaut scene".

Fadiman first heard of microdosing from a Californian neighbour, the psychedelic enthusiast Robert Forte. Forte told him, or so Fadiman recalled, that the discoverer of LSD, Swiss chemist Albert Hofmann, had used low doses of LSD regularly. He later realized that what he recalled of what Robert Forte had told him was not quite right (see Chapter 4). Forte had not said that Hoffman used these low doses regularly, nor did he tell him that Hoffman took doses as low as 10 µg. Hofmann actually used doses between 20 and 50 µg, which have a very different range of effects.

Fadiman, however, began asking people if they had ever used doses of 10 µg, and if they had or if they would like to, he would very much like to know their experiences. He began to accumulate their reports, which indicated that there were clear indications that people generally described benefits from these extremely low doses.

The first idea of more general research came after Fadiman gave a talk in Denver about psychedelics in general, and his own new interest in what he called "milddoses". He met a woman, later referred to as "Madeline", who told him how taking these very low doses of LSD enhanced her everyday performance. She had been microdosing for some years, taking a dose on average six times each month. After he met Madeline, Fadiman came across another person reporting on this longer-term use of LSD, and these reports were reproduced in his book about many aspects of psychedelic research. (Fadiman 2011: 199–205). At the same Denver talk, someone came up afterwards and suggested mailing out samples of LSD in microdose quantities and asking people to report on their experiences using these microdoses over a full month. Over the next few months, the person in Denver forwarded him a number of these reports. They included accounts of improved focus, energy and creativity, as well as alleviation of depression.

He then began to develop a protocol for a self-study of microdosing that would maximize safety and would allow for some systematic reporting of experiences. His informants provided evidence that the day after a microdose day was often better than the first day. Therefore, Fadiman developed a three-day model. On day 1 of every cycle, the participants would take 10 µg and keep their usual everyday schedule of work, meals, exercise and social activities. They were instructed to monitor their mood, physical state, symptoms, productivity, mental focus, creativity and the ease with which they did their work.

After each day, they would write a few notes about how the day went and what happened in respect to the factors mentioned above. On days 2 and 3, participants should not take LSD, but continue with monitoring their mental state and reporting on it. The third day provided a recurring set-point to better evaluate the experience. It also reduced the chance of developing tolerance to the psychedelic. Here is what Fadiman has said about his dosing regimen:

> *I have suggested this for a period of one month. The reasoning behind that schedule is that early reports, including my own experiences, suggested that the effects of the microdose lasted over two days. Many people have reported that the second day is actually*

the better one for them. The third day, for research purposes, and for self-exploration, was to allow most people to return to their baseline and their normal level of functioning. When they would then take a new dose, they would be more aware of the difference between their baseline and whatever they felt taking the microdose. After a month, everyone was counseled to decide on their own dosing schedule and to let us know what they decided and how well it worked. Most of our healthy subjects actually microdose less often; a number of our depressed subjects moved to every other day, and people change their dose levels both up and down. Many people also reported that by the end of 10 doses, the schedule was also good for them and so they kept to it. My one day on two days off suggestion was never intended to be considered optimal. It was a research protocol that has been fruitful. It also, of course, maximized safety and prevented tolerance. I did have those variables and mind when I put together that protocol, but it was primarily designed to most easily explore the effects of microdosing over a wide range of people and conditions. For that, it has proved to be excellent.

(Fadiman 2018)

By 2015, Fadiman had accumulated several file drawers of reports and also discovered some use of microdosing among younger tech workers in Silicon Valley.

A brief article about microdosing appeared in the widely distributed *Rolling Stone* magazine, which included the comments of a machine designer who claimed: "Microdosing has helped me come up with some new designs to explore new ways of thinking." He also said: "You would be surprised at how many people are actually doing it" (Leonard, 2015). A deluge of media reports spun out from this article and more media attention led to more users, which again led to more immediate attention. In this way, the phenomena—if indeed it was ever limited to it—escaped Silicon Valley.

Systematic data collection on microdosing

Sophia Korb, PhD, who had worked with Fadiman some years earlier on a survey among students about the nature and extent of their psychedelic experimentation, joined up with him again with the goal of doing more systematic research. Fadiman, by that time, was being overwhelmed with requests for information and compiling the ever-increasing number of reports, claims, and questions—often from desperate people—sent to him.

Korb took on the serious work of moving from notes to data, from individual requests to a website, from isolated stories to checklists, from early random searches to a more focused approach. They understood and took into account the unconventional aspects of this research. It was closer to a biologist determining what kinds of plants grew in a particular area, than well-controlled laboratory research on pharmaceutical agents. As all of the participants were not only voluntary, but provided their own substances, while Fadiman and Korb recommended dose size and frequency, they accepted reports that differed in both. In so doing, they found that many people preferred to lower the dose below 10 μg, while some others increased the frequency to every other day. Whatever one thinks about the validity of this dataset, it points to regular patterns of changed behaviour and helps explore this new realm of microdoses.

The actual format of the study had participants fill in a standardized (very simple) protocol with some notes. On the days that were drug-free (days two and three), they would also fill-in the Positive And Negative Affect Schedule (PANAS), a self-report questionnaire that consists of two 10-item scales to measure both positive and negative affect. Each item is rated on a Likert scale from 0 (not at all) to 3 (very much). The PANAS is a standard psychological instrument to measure mood states. Participants were also asked to give a synoptic report at the end of each month. Another group of participants did not take any drugs, but did the same reporting and measures and were used as a comparison group. From a strictly scientific point of view, such a study is not methodologically acceptable because of its many uncontrolled variables, as well as selection bias. Fadiman and Korb are conscious of these problems and state that they are not trying to prove or disprove specific hypotheses but are discovering the range of possible effects (Fadiman, and Korb, 2018a). They have gathered more than 1,850 reports to date (July 2018) and are working to systematize them, prepare articles and publish a book about microdosing for the general public.

Fadiman and Korb recently reported several surprises, with people describing positive effects of microdosing on halting or minimizing the symptoms of premenstrual syndrome (Fadiman and Korb 2018a). They are also supporting more formal medical and psychiatric research on microdosing with LSD and psilocybin. They consider their research project a form of "Citizen Science" similar in intention, if not in form, to a phase 2 clinical trial, attempting to evaluate if psychedelics at these low-dose levels produce any significant benefits (cf. Waldman 2017: 110).

5

Claims about the Effects of Microdosing

In spite of all the claims made about microdosing in recent years, there has been no solid evidence given for any of the claimed effects. There are problems with the kind of "anecdotal" evidence which appears as self-reports on the Internet. Firstly, there is no proof that these people have really taken LSD, as they usually have no definitive evidence of the substance's identity and purity. Another problem is the actual quantity of the dose, which cannot be accurately known with preparations from illegal sources. This is especially difficult when it comes to target-oriented dosing at slightly below or above threshold subjective effects, e.g. 15–30 µg. That means it would only take a very small inaccuracy of 5–10 µg to be below or above threshold. Not many scales can measure those tiny amounts exactly, and the accuracy is not improved when it comes to cutting a slice of paper from a "blotter" paper of an illegal LSD preparation.

In one of the chapters of the present book, the placebo problem is evaluated. This is a reaction mainly determined by expectation and environment rather than resulting from the drug's actual physiological effects. It is well known as a powerful consequence in conventional pharmaceutical research and is usually avoided by making the researcher, as well as his experimental subjects, "blind" to the condition which the individual subject will confront during the experiment (i.e. whether they are taking an active or inactive dose). This is called a "double-blind" experiment, and it is the gold standard of scientific evaluation of a pharmacologically active substance. An experiment is called "placebo-controlled" when a placebo is given to compare its effect with the "real drug". With respect to microdosing, nobody would argue that the subjectively perceivable effects are minimal, if not non-existent. Especially with the very low "sub-perceptual" doses taken with microdosing, the "placebo effects" will be hard (or impossible) to differentiate from real drug effects.

To describe effects of a drug, it is important to differentiate between acute, sub-acute, and chronic drug effects. *Acute effects* of a drug are those which appear under the direct influence of the drug's effects on the organism. Acute effects are over when the concentration of the drug is so low that no effects are generated by the drug's interaction with the organism. *Subacute effects* are those which can be seen with some drugs after the molecules have left the organism (or have been metabolized into other molecules), but some aftereffects can still be felt. With respect to psychedelic drugs, it is well-known that an "afterglow" can follow the acute effects of a drug-induced psychedelic experience (with higher doses). *Chronic effects* are those effects which result after the organism has adapted to the drug after an initial equilibration/adaption phase. Chronic effects only appear when the drug is given on a regular basis, e.g. daily.

With respect to the claims made about microdosing, one can find claims about *acute*, *subacute* and *chronic* (long-term) effects. Because these are all subjective descriptions, and given that most of the descriptions have been produced under uncontrolled conditions (e.g. unverified quality and dose of drug, widely varied environmental circumstances), all descriptions of effects will be treated as "claims" here.

Claims about acute effects

The claims about acute effects refer to better performance with respect to cognition, mood, interpersonal behaviour and creativity whilst under the acute effects of the drug.

With respect to "better performance" typical claims like the following have been made: "I was able to shut out virtually distracting influences" or "I was impressed with the intensity of concentration, the forcefulness and exuberance with which I could proceed toward the solution" (Austin 2018: 110). According to Austin (2018: 110), in an unsystematic survey on his website The Third Wave, 229 individuals ranked the results of microdosing on various aspects of their performance on a scale of 1 to 6. Respondents gave an average score of 4.65 for span of focus, 4.57 for problem solving, and 4.76 for creativity. For general mood, MD reported an average score of 5.2. (Austin 2018: 110).

A typical positive claim about the acute effects on creative performance goes like this: "Microdosing makes me more productive and gives me outside-the-box thinking," says Alex. "When programming, it's useful to just see how the logic is supposed to flow. It's like if you were playing chess and were able to see a few more steps ahead than normal ..." (Alex quoted in Bewellbuzz 2016). Many of the claims about acute effects circle around "enhanced creativity" with microdosing. "It gives you fresh eyes, for programming or figuring out algorithmic stuff. It made me really productive in a motivated way. Whatever mental block that was stopping me from doing something would disappear" (microdoser, quoted in Cruz 2016: 26). Paul Austin, a proponent of microdosing, took his first microdose of 15 µg at a friend's wedding. He "felt instantly more at ease"—he was comfortable interacting with other guests and was more empathic and less inhibited. "Microdosing gave me the sense of being content and OK with who I am", he explains. … "It helped me achieve flow states", he says, referring to the productivity boost that accompanies being "'in the zone', freed of distraction" (Austin, quoted in Pathak 2017). However, Austin's description contains some aspects which suggest that the effects experienced were those of a minidose, not a microdose. Others have described the effects of microdosing as "a little activating" and compared its effects with Adderall (amphetamine) or Ritalin (methylphenidate) but much less intense (Waldman 2017). "It's like Adderall but without the side effects" (Fadiman in Gregoire 2016). Similarities with the wake-promoting drug modafinil, which has less notable effects than the other two drugs mentioned above, have also been suggested (Garcia 2016).

Claims about sub-acute and chronic effects

In most of the subjective descriptions of the effects of microdosing there is no clear distinction between acute and sub-acute effects. However, Fadiman's descriptions of the effects of microdosing (if the users follow the Fadiman protocol with dosing every fourth day for a month) imply that some effects can be "carried over" to the next day or two after a microdose has been taken. Unfortunately there are no descriptions available which have taken the effort to make a clear distinction between acute effects on dosing days and sub-acute/chronic effects on the non-drug days. Here is a typical self-description of acute and subacute effects claimed to be produced by LSD microdosing:

> *Microdosing has allowed me to unlock my potential and to live fuller, to be engaged in an individual moment, which has in turn allowed me to be more focused and happier. I'm much more empathetic and willing to give people the benefit of the doubt now. I just feel lighter all the time, even on day 3 of the routine. I rarely get angry or stressed anymore. Since I've started microdosing, I've been eating much healthier and exercising more. And it hasn't been forced. I started doing yoga and meditating daily rather organically. It all just happened.* (Anonymous, quoted in Fadiman 2016: 58).

In respect to the chronic effects of microdosing, one of Austin's respondents stated: "I was no longer sensitive to criticism or confrontations, my work ethic improved and I was much more open and caring for customers and coworkers. It became less about me and more about the collective" (Austin 2018: 111). After microdosing LSD twice a week for more than seven months, Austin (2018: 145) himself reported that he "had gone off without a hitch: my creative projects flourished, I had more confidence and charisma in social situations, and I excelled in my ability to articulate thoughts and ideas in a clear, meaningful manner". In his book, Fadiman (2011) states that with respect to the claimed effects of microdosing, he hasn't come to "any general conclusions about these low doses beyond noting that all the reports in my files indicate, as these individuals have, that the low-dose use has been positive." ... "It's as if your body, which always has your best interest in mind in spite of you, gets a larger number of votes". Elsewhere in the book he says that "... What seems to happen with microdosing is that you're more attuned to your own real needs" (Gregoire & Fadiman 2016).

Claims about effects on pathological conditions

With respect to "treating" pathological conditions such as anxiety and depression, it has been stated by microdosers that it "helps manage my anxiety both in the short and long term" (Bewellbuzz 2016, Fadiman in Gregoire 2016). Fadiman and Korb (2018) reported that "the largest group of people who write us are people with depression and treatment-resistant depression". Out of an initial 418 respondents, 35% cited depression as the reason they began microdosing and 27% cited anxiety, while 58% said they were motivated by a combination of depression and anxiety (quoted in Austin 2018: 33). Reports on effects of depressive states typically go this way: "I have fought depression for some 6–7 years since adolescence, microdosing has, so far, consistently helped me get on with my day-to-day, just as much on no MD [microdose] days as MD days. This also applies to Social and General Anxiety which has been less severe but experienced for the same period". This statement is congruent with Fadiman's observation that "... for most people, the effects last two days, and for some people, the second day was better" (Fadiman 2016: 57). Another report goes: "I overcame my depression with microdosing because I can consistently be productive and happy with it as a creative booster. It also eliminates any anxiety I get because I never used to raise my hand in class. I smoke a lot of cannabis and it's unhealthy to overindulge. I found microdosing to make me feel the need to be productive so I smoke much less when I microdose and don't indulge just to smoke" (Austin 2017). Fadiman's view is that at such low doses, psychedelics should be viewed more like anti-depressants and cognitive enhancers (Fadiman, quoted in Bewellbuzz 2016).

More recently, Fadiman received a report from a person who suffered from chronic back pain for years. He started microdosing with LSD and mescaline and reported that even with the first dose the pain disappeared and after two weeks of microdosing he was nearly pain-free. Unfortunately, no exact dosing regimenwas given (Fadiman 2018c). It has long been known from early studies, where LSD was given as an active placebo to compare its effects to an inactive placebo and different pain medications, that LSD can influence pain perception by modulating attentional processing. However, those studies were done with much higher doses (Kast 1964).

Results from studies with very low doses of LSD

From these experiments done using very low doses of LSD (5–20 μg), the following can be scientifically concluded.

In the microdosing range (10–20 μg LSD):

Psychological state and neurocognition
- No perceptible subjective effects (5–15 μg)
- No effects detectable by outside observers (10–20 μg)
- No measurable cognitive deficits (10–20 μg)

Physiological effects
- No changes in temperature, blood pressure, pulse or respiratory rate
- Pupil diameter changes (10 μg)
- Alterations of galvanic skin response (10 μg)
- Increased adrenaline levels probable (20 μg)
- Extension of REM sleep (dreaming) (20 μg)

It is impossible to go into details here about the many (more than 25) scientific studies that have used minidoses of LSD (25–50 μg). The reader is referred to Chapter 8 for details. The results from those studies can be summarized as follows.

Neurocognitive
- Impairment in most neurocognitive measures
- Decrease in intelligence measures
- No increase in neurocognitive measures
- Increased performance in psychomotor tasks (few people)

Psychological
- Mental irritation
- Increase in moods
- Psychological labilization
- Loss of train of thought
- Unmotivated smiling
- Enhanced closed-eyes imagery
- Increased anxiety
- Occasional cathartic reactions (laughing, weeping etc.)
- Increased perception of feelings/motives of others (sometimes)

Physiological
- No change in temperature, blood pressure, pulse and respiratory rate
- Change of handwriting style
- Increased adrenaline levels
- Extension of REM sleep phases (dreaming)

Repeatedly made claims about effects of microdosing

Until such a time when scientifically designed placebo-controlled studies have been carried out, no valid data yet exist about the effects of microdosing. We do not know which claims contain some truth, and which are coming from merely subjective impressions, self-deception, or placebo effects. It is clear that proponents of microdosing, especially those who are likely to benefit financially from "helping others to microdose" or writing booklets about the subject, might tend to make more positive—and possibly exaggerated—claims. We also do not know much about people who have tried microdosing without any effect, because those people will probably not report this absence of effect. Early enthusiasts of other "neuroenhancement" drugs or devices have been proven in the past to produce false and exaggerated claims (Partridge et al. 2011).

The following paragraphs should be read with these limitations in mind. I have tried to list all claims made in relevant publications. I have differentiated claims regarding effects on performance and those describing effects on pathological conditions.

Claimed effects on performance
- Improved work (amount, flow, quality, enjoyment) (Fadiman 2016)
- Increased productivity (Austin in Grob Plante 2017)
- Enhancement of focus (Fadiman in Gregoire 2016, Woods 2016)
- Work more pleasurable (Woods 2016)
- More ease to gain flow states (Austin 2017)
- Increased creativity (Fadiman 2016)
- Better listener, more empathy for others (Woods 2016, Bewellbuzz 2016, Matrixblogger 2017)
- More happy and social (Bewellbuzz 2016)
- Capacity to live in the present (the now) (Fadiman 2016)

- More attuned to your own real needs (Gregoire and Fadiman 2016)
- Increased health habits: food choices, exercise, yoga meditation (Fadiman 2011)
- More relaxed and better focus (Cruz 2017)

Claimed effects on pathological conditions
- Alleviates anxiety (general and social) (Fadiman 2016, Bewellbuzz 2016, Austin 2017, Denton 2017)
- Alleviates depression (Fadiman 2011, Waldman 2017, Cruz 2016)
- Decreases or helps to stop: cigarettes, coffee, Adderall, Venlafaxine (Fadiman 2016)

Claims that have been made only one or two times

This second list includes all claims about effects of microdosing that I came across during the year of my research into this subject. These were made in only one or two publications or internet entries. I have included them all to provide a comprehensive overview. They may also serve as advice for pointing to possible applications. Again, this is not a list of recommended uses, it is just a list of claims which have been made under uncontrolled conditions often by unknown individuals.

Claimed effects on performance
- Improvement of learning: languages, advanced maths (Fadiman 2016)
- Fuller awareness of entanglement of ideas (richer and higher overview and increased associations) (Cruz 2016)
- Focused attention in class (Fadiman 2016)
- Enhanced pattern recognition (Fadiman in Bewellbuzz 2016)
- Increased mental acuity (Austin in Grob Plante 2017)
- Able to see a few more steps ahead, like playing chess (Alex quoted in Bewellbuzz 2016)
- Seeing more pieces at once of a problem to be solved (Fadiman in Bewellbuzz 2016)
- Increased outside-the-box thinking (Alex quoted in Bewellbuzz 2016)
- Easy and lazy mood (Matrixblogger 2017)

- More feelings (Matrixblogger 2017)
- Personal and work-related insights (Fadiman 2016)
- Opening of the heart (Woods 2016)
- Improved relationship to body (Fadiman in Gregoire 2016, Woods 2016)
- Appreciation for simple/little things (Bewellbuzz 2016, Cruz 2016)
- Living more in the here and now (Austin 2017)
- More mindfulness (Woods 2016)
- Enhanced emotional clarity (Cruz 2016)
- Music is better (Cruz 2016)
- Incapable of worrying about tomorrow or next week (Austin 2017)
- Procrastination lessened (Fadiman 2016)
- Increased self-improvement (Austin 2017)
- Improvement of spiritual awareness (Austin 2017)
- Allows one to drink more alcohol (Woods 2016, Denton 2017)
- Inability to eat unhealthy food (Bewellbuzz 2016)
- Improvement of physical skills (music playing, flying a plane, driving) (Fadiman 2016)
- Being able to walk long distances without tiring
- Improvement of athletic performance (Austin 2017)

Claimed effects on pathological conditions
- Decreased impulsivity (Waldman 2017)
- Improving symptoms of ADHD (Fadiman in Gregoire 2016, Austin 2017)
- Menstrual periods: elimination of pain and cramping (Fadiman 2016)
- Trauma: decreased triggering (Fadiman 2016)
- Asperger's syndrome: more ease in social situations (Fadiman 2016)
- Bipolar: mood elevation during depressive phase (Fadiman 2016)
- Migraines: lessened or eliminated (Fadiman 2016)
- Ending of ice-pick headache (one-minute clusters) (Fadiman 2016)
- Internet addiction stopped (Woods 2016)
- Stuttering: increased fluency (Fadiman 2016)
- Less smoking (Denton 2017)
- Less alcohol drinking (Denton 2017)
- Helps with writer's block and first drafts (Fadiman 2016)

- Less binge eating (Denton 2017)
- Allows reduction of ADHD medication (Fadiman in Bewellbuzz 2016)
- Easier to come off psychopharmaceuticals (Fadiman in Gregoire 2016)
- Allows reduction of pain and/or sleep medication (Austin 2017)

Conclusions

If one considers all the positive claims made for microdosing (and, on occasion, minidosing—whether this slightly larger dose occurs intentionally or accidentally), it sounds too good to be true. The lists above read like this practice is a kind of panacea to cope with all the problems a modern American confronts at her workplace or in their personal life (or with a variety of endemic mental illnesses, like anxiety or depression). It seems highly probable that most of these claims, especially those only mentioned one or a very few times, are not based on factual changes, but more on wishful thinking, placebo responses, or lively imagination.

It is unlikely that these extremely low doses could favorably affect such a wide range of conditions, but it is no less unlikely that thousands of individuals, many being mental health and medical professionals, and most with considerable prior experience using psychedelics in high doses would have such consistent reports about the effects if such effects did not exist. Thankfully, traditional double-blind, university-sponsored studies are underway to seriously study these possible effects. Therefore it is likely that within the next few years we will be able to definitively distinguish, using traditional and fully accepted scientific methods, the actual from the imaginary effects of microdosing.

6

Subjective Experiences

6.1 Microdosing (5–20 µg)

One of the two definitions of microdosing is of a dose where no subjective—or virtually no subjective—effects can be detected, (a "sub-perceptual dose"). This implies a dose of LSD in the range of 5–20 µg. As suggested by the term "sub-perceptual", at a dose of less than 20 µg nothing can be felt or detected with respect to subjective effects. It is therefore, virtually impossible to describe acute effects at this dose. However, if one looks at all the claims made for effects of microdosing, it appears obvious that although a lot of people tend to refer to microdosing as taking "sub-perceptual" doses, their reports describe acute effects which they have subjectively perceived. There are two potential explanations: 1. They felt no subjective effects immediately, but they believed their work performance was nevertheless affected. It is conceivable that this was caused by alterations of processes that exist on a level below the one where direct subjective effects can be felt. 2. They simply took a dose that was above the threshold for subjective effects, which produced some mild subjective effects and maybe effects on their work or everyday performance. If one looks at the description of "A typical day when microdosing" as given by a prominent proponent of microdosing, it's obvious that effects of a non-"sub-perceptual" dose are being described (see below). Besides the serious problem of verifying dose and quality of the drug taken, these unclear definitions (and resulting effects) contribute to confusion and make a scientific evaluation of microdosing difficult to impossible.

There are clear problems on how best to characterize the effect or lack of effect of a microdose. The now-defunct term "sub-perceptual", was originally suggested by Fadiman since microdoses do not elicit the classic perceptual exaggerations and distortions that occur with higher doses of psychedelics. It does not mean, though, that individuals taking microdoses cannot perceive any subjective, cognitive, emotional, and in many cases physical changes from their base state.

Acute and chronic effects

Before proceeding further, it makes sense to differentiate between acute and chronic effects of a drug. *Acute effects* refer to effects which appear during the hours when a drug is in the organism and which reveal its activity. In the case of LSD the acute effects usually begin 30–90 minutes after the oral administration of the drug and last 5–10 hours, depending on dose. *Chronic effects* are those which appear when a drug is taken on a regular basis, e.g. daily or every few days. Acute and chronic effects can sometimes differ significantly with many drugs and pharmaceuticals. In respect to microdosing we are dealing with possible *acute* effects as well as *chronic* effects of regular dosing (e.g. two doses per week).

What is the dose at which an acute drug effect can be detected?

In the first clinical trial with LSD, psychiatrist Arthur Stoll (1947) found 20 µg to be undetectable in most cases, whereas 30 µg produced some light symptoms, peaking at 2.5–3.5 hours. Greiner et al. (1958) found subjective effects which were reliably felt above 20 µg. Whilst some of their data are unclear, they suggest subjective effects with lower doses. Canadian psychiatrist Abram Hoffer's subjects did not detect 15 µg, whereas the majority could feel effects of a 25 µg dose (Hoffer and Osmond 1967). Savage (1955) reported from a non-blind observational study that some subjects were able to detect 10 µg. In conclusion, detectable effects begin for most people at 25 µg, for some at 20 µg, with 15 µg not reliably detectable from a scientific point of view. Scientific studies usually use the mean as the measure, so that although in a study some subjects might react to a drug, their reactions dissipate into the mean—and the mean might not show a large enough difference to be significantly higher than a result by chance and thus counted as "no difference" (with respect to the mean). It is possible that quantitative data alone are not sufficient when it comes to smaller, more subtle effects in subjects with different sensitivities.

Abramson et al. (1956) have conducted studies in which two young and healthy LSD-experienced volunteers were given 5, 10, or 20 µg LSD on a daily basis for up to six days. The authors reported "no reaction" with doses of 5, 10, and 20 µg. However, it is probable that the development of tolerance to LSD had an impact on the results with the 20, 50, and 75 µg doses, as these were given a few days after the administration of the lower doses.

Effects of very low-dose LSD studied by the US Air Force

For unknown purposes, a low-dose LSD study sponsored by the US Air Force Office of Scientific Research was conducted to detect very low doses of LSD by physiological parameters and psychological (self) observation. One might speculate if this study had another possible threat in mind: the slow, low-dose intoxication of the masses by an enemy.

Fourteen young men without apparent emotional problems participated. 24 doses were given. Physiological measurements (20 minutes of each hour) were done while subjects reclined in a dark room. Another 20 minutes of each hour were devoted to psychiatric observation. "In the remaining intervals subjects occupied themselves in any way they chose". Conscious mood was assessed by two questionnaires constructed from the authors "initial experiments", about which, unfortunately, no details are given. It also remains unknown whether the subjects of the published study took part in these "initial experiments" or if they were drug-naïve to LSD. Two self-designed questionnaires were used in the experiments. On one of them, subjects estimated deviations from their usual state of perception, body image, alertness, emotion, and thought. On the other questionnaire "the subject placed himself along the scale between pairs of adjectives describing opposite extremes of mood". No examples of the items used were given by the authors. Psychiatric interviews were repeated every hour. Limitations of this study were the unknown number of "initial experiments" the subjects took part in previous to the described study. Subjects were said to be "generally aware of the LSD effects in the usual dose range", but none knew the dose of their oral dose, or whether they had taken a placebo. This description implies that the *researchers were not blind* about the drugs given to the subjects. Therefore this has to be termed a blind study, but the experiment does not meet the gold standard of pharmacological research, which is the double-blind experiment, in which both subjects and researchers are blind to the fact of whether a drug (or placebo) is given on the experimental day. Another limitation was the non-balanced design (only three subjects got placebo, whilst ten received LSD in different doses). The measures used (self-designed questionnaires, not specifically trained psychiatric interviewers) were not validated—as is necessary for any valid scientific study—in order to remove suggestibility prompted by the items listed. There were too few subjects for a reliable study, and data collection and statistics for exclusion of chance results could not be carried out. Nevertheless the study appears to provide some interesting results, which will be reported here in detail.

The first questionnaire, about different forms of subjective symptoms, was done by two subjects on 20 µg, showing "deviations from normal in body image, thought, emotion at the second and third hour". Four subjects did this questionnaire with a 7 µg dose and reported no symptoms. The second questionnaire, designed by Greiner et al., was based on their "initial" experiments (unpublished) as a "bipolar scale between pairs of adjectives describing opposite states of mood", also called the "adjective check list". The four subjects on 20 µg LSD marked the scales in such a way as to give a *decrease* in dimensions labeled alertness, motility, control, thought, and sociability during the entire dosing day. After 7 µg, subjects showed "for alertness and motility a dip in the third hour followed by a climb above the initial value for the rest of the day. Control and thought sank gradually for the first three hours, returning to the initial level at the fourth hour. Sociability increased for the first two hours, dipped sharply at the third hour, and recovered to remain far above the pre-drug value. The sixth dimension, hedonic tone, also dipped sharply at the third hour and bounced far above the initial level for the rest of the day" (Greiner et al. 1958: 209).

Psychopathology and Psychophysiology of Minimal LSD-25 Dosage

A Preliminary Dosage-Response Spectrum

THEODORE GREINER, M.D.; NEIL R. BURCH, M.D., and ROBERT EDELBERG, Ph.D., Houston, Texas

Despite 14 years of investigation, as intensive as accorded any biologically active chemical, a gap remains in the systematic description of human response to lysergic acid diethylamide (LSD-25). The dramatic schizophrenic-like symptoms after doses of 40µg to 100µg have drawn the main interest. The threshold for activity is placed at 20µg by general consensus, while perfunctory administration of smaller doses has left their effect uncertain.

Accompanying those pharmacologic demonstrations has been the controversy whether LSD symptoms simulate the psychopathology of schizophrenia [1] or can be better explained as a toxic organic psychosis.[2] One of these alternatives might be favored by its resemblance to the complete dosage-response relationship of LSD. It is unfortunate for analogical comparison that early stages of toxic psychosis have rarely been described in a psychopathological framework [3]; on the other hand, there is a firm basis for comparison with various schizophrenic processes.

This preliminary note reports the response to 24 doses of LSD-25, graduated in size to emphasize the relationship of symptoms to dosage.

Methods

Fourteen young men without apparent emotional problems volunteered as subjects. Extensive

Submitted for publication June 27, 1957.

Department of Psychiatry and Neurology, Baylor University College of Medicine, Texas Medical Center.

This research was supported by the U. S. Air Force through the Air Force Office of Scientific Research of the Air Research and Development Command under Contract No. AF 18(603)-79.

208

physiological measurements on the subjects reclining alone in a dark room took 20 minutes of each hour. Another third of each hour was absorbed in psychological and psychiatric observation. In the remaining intervals subjects occupied themselves in any way they chose. Conscious mood was assessed by two questionnaires constructed from our initial experiments. On one questionnaire, the subject estimated deviation from his usual state in matters of perception, body image, alertness, emotion, and thought. On the other, the subject placed himself along the scale between pairs of adjectives describing opposite extremes of mood.

A psychiatric interview preceded the dose and was repeated every hour during the experimental day. While the subjects were generally aware of LSD symptoms in usual dosage, none knew the size of their oral dose, or whether they had taken a placebo of plain purified water U. S. P. The "double-blind" system prevailed, in that all measurements and judgments were made without knowledge of the dose.

Results

Physiological changes in general were absent with doses below 20µg. The exception was the nonspecific component of the galvanic skin response (GSR), which was activated after 7µg (Figure).

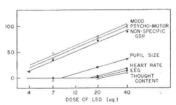

Effect of LSD dosage on psychiatric and physiological measures. The relative intensity of LSD effects on an arbitrary ordinate are plotted against dose on a logarithmic scale. Measurements are described in the text.

In respect to the psychiatric interviews, after one hour the six subjects on the 20 µg dose exhibited,

> ... *hypomanic behavior with euphoria, increased psychomotor tension, and distractability. By the second hour there was indifference with physical retardation and social withdrawal, irritability, and frequent forced*

laughter without pleasure. At the third hour withdrawal continued with prominent shifts in affect, and changes in thought process, including feelings of inferiority, obsessive thinking, strange unreal thoughts, and one early idea of reference. By the fourth hour most of the subjects were mildly hypomanic and continued that way, with occasional waves of depression or irritability. ... In the case of six subjects who received 7 μg psychiatric interview in the first and second hours recorded hypomania with expansive euphoria, increased psychomotor activity and tension, and irritability. By the third hour there appeared sudden profound tiredness with an appropriate degree of indifference and depression of mood. At the fourth hour, when subjects were convinced that the drug effects were over, hypomania of a characteristic egosyntonic type [i.e. felt as belonging to the persons usual state] developed. ... Hypomania continued through the rest of the day with occasional waves of depression. There were no changes of either thought processes or of thought content after 7 μg (six subjects), after 4 μg (two subjects), or after 12 μg (two subjects). However, nine out of those ten subjects displayed cycles of sudden and profound shifts in affect. They ranged toward both extremes of mood during the day; no one experienced severe euphoria who did not also have a high degree of dysphoria at some other time. The three subjects who received purified water placebo reported isolated symptoms of tenseness, preoccupation, and change in body image, particularly in the first two hours. The only '50%' symptom for the group was mild sleepiness during the third and fourth hours.

(Greiner et al. 1958: 209)

Cycles in affect and in psychomotor activity were detected by psychiatric interviews only and by the adjective check list, but not the other questionnaire. It is noteworthy that subjects under low doses of LSD were not completely aware of these cycles. In their conclusions, the authors refer to Stoll's (1947) report on the changes on affectivity, but refer to their observed affective lability and wave-like shifting of mood as "the mental consequence of low-dose LSD".

Subjective experiences

The material that will follow here looks a little fragmented as it gives accounts from different users and modes of use (erratic versus regular), and includes acute and chronic effects. Efforts have been taken to mix a "representative sample of impressions". Even if some aspects are produced by placebo or nocebo effects, some others might be related to possible "objective" effects of microdosing. Until more comprehensive scientific studies are carried out we don't know the magnitude of the possible placebo effect.

Another fact must be mentioned. We have no descriptions from all the people that have experienced "nothing" with microdosing. They did not experience anything different from usual and have nothing to report.

Effects with a verified microdose of 12.5 µg

The following report came from a person experienced with LSD, who had the LSD he used tested in a toxicological laboratory. He did not feel much alteration from the dose of 12.5 µg LSD, but wrote this short protocol:

- 10:05 am. Ingestion of 12.5 µg LSD per os.
- 12:40 pm. No effects felt (going out for a meal).
- 3:30 pm. Minimal effects felt, but only if attention is directed inward. Minimal effects also in nature, but really minimal, if there.

Experiences with different low doses of LSD

This report came from a person who posted his experiences on the internet (Garcia 2016). The reporting user thinks he took low doses of LSD for a few days in a row. He gives the following account of his experiences:

> **Day 1**: I took ~5 µg LSD. After an hour I didn't notice
> any difference, so I took another dose (~10 µg in total).
> I still didn't notice much of an effect ...

Day 2: I tried ~15 μg. Again, I didn't feel much, so I took more (~20 μg total). I soon felt it 'hit' me. It was like a gentle touch. Just a slightly different state of consciousness. I felt motivated, as if everything was going well. Speaking to my roommate, they said I seemed generally more talkative.

Day 3: I took ~20 μg. Later in the day, I found myself walking around with a permanent smile, like I literally couldn't stop smiling. I just felt happy. I didn't feel like I was drunk or high—just like I was having a good day. I went to bed in a good mood and woke up happy.

Day 4: I tried taking ~30 μg. I did not feel great afterward. It felt like being drunk, as if I chugged a beer or two. Except I felt more in control. I still felt a little disorientated. I didn't get much, if any, work done as I couldn't focus.

Day 5: I took today off. I didn't feel strong effects from the previous day, but still felt something.

Day 6: I took 20 μg again. Life is good. I don't feel drunk, nor high. I just feel right. The day went by fast because I was having a good time. I also noticed that I had more energy and felt more awake.

Austin's idealized description of the effects of a microdose

Paul Austin is a proponent of microdosing and offers paid consultantship about microdosing. On his website, Austin (2017) claims to describe a typical day when microdosing:

09:00 – INCREASED CREATIVE OUTPUT
- *Brilliant outbursts in work and personal creative projects.*
- *Super easy to get in the ZONE.*
- *Work becomes fun!*

16:00 – MORE PHYSICAL ENERGY
- *More stamina while exercising.*
- *Clean energy buzz–like a psychedelic coffee.*

- *Lift heavier weights*
- *Improved coordination & higher level of focus.*

19:00 – IMPROVED EMOTIONAL BALANCE
- *Create stronger bonds with new and existing friends*
- *High levels of gratitude*
- *Alleviates Depression*
- *Gradual buildup of openness and awareness*

21:00 – HEIGHTENED SPIRITUAL AWARENESS
- *Glimmers of insight into the unity of all life forms*
- *Amazed by the wonders of life*
- *More in line with spiritual intentions*

If one looks at Austin's description, it appears that doses have been taken that produced some perceptible effects, which would imply minidosing instead of microdosing.

Acute effects of microdosing and creativity

In my personal net of relationships, I came across a person who it seems had a "creativity experience" with a very low dose of LSD (which was verified to be 15 µg LSD).

> *I had thought about meditation as a possible method*
> *for gaining insights, in the philosophical context, that*
> *might enable intuitive—and therefore as yet unknown—*
> *connections to emerge. With this in mind, lying down*
> *and starting from a basic meditation exercise, I entered*
> *into a state of 'receiving' aphorisms that emerged, of*
> *the kind I have already frequently written about. The*
> *resulting sentences/aphorisms are, of course, not all*
> *truly profound, but they fascinated me with regard to*
> *the process by which they arose. I noticed in amazement*
> *how a sentence, starting from the first word—at which*
> *point I still had no idea of the direction in which the*

sentence was heading—would unfold, word by word, right to the end without any help from me and would present itself to me as a virtually complete sentence. In the process, I experienced the 'creative rush' as an act of effortless observation. With ease, grammatical structures seemed to develop of their own accord, simultaneously carrying with them content that was new and unfamiliar to me. The sentences arose, with short breaks for recalling them and writing them down, over the course of approximately one hour. During the creative state, I was in an emotionally balanced and calm to slightly excited mood, which I experienced as positive; at the same time, I felt unusually rational and clear.

In spite of the hype for using microdosing to enhance creativity, these kinds of more detailed descriptions cannot be found on internet platforms, where statements are usually limited to only a few words.

Reports on long-term effects of microdosing

It seems that it is not easy to get hold of descriptions made about the effects of microdosing which qualify as serious and sufficiently detailed descriptions. I have surfed through hundreds of internet entries, but only came across descriptions comprised of one or two sentences at most. For example, on the fourth most viewed YouTube video about microdosing, the maker noticed many benefits from microdosing mushrooms for a longer period (not specified) as he felt "clean energy while not being too stimulating, mental focus, cognitive function and mood improved; 'mental clarity', 'emotional balance', 'positive mental attitude', [and] 'improved overall well-being'" (Hupli 2018).

A respondent to the survey of Fadiman and Krob (2018) reported, with respect to enhanced everyday performance with regular microdosing: "I am feeling very energetic, very focused, very alert. It's the same as taking amphetamine, but without the jittery or the crash after, so that's wonderful".

Another person, seemingly with some mental health issues, wrote to them: "I have noticed that my 'mental chatter' is considerably less ... It was nearly constant before, and not very positive. First thing every morning on my mind was always a raging flood of responsibilities, reminders, and thoughts unnecessary. … Now my thoughts are quiet and calm with a gentle flow" (Korb 2018).

Sophia Korb and Jim Fadiman have conducted an exploratory survey to evaluate effects of regular microdosing for longer time periods. Initially, they asked their subjects to submit 30 days of data. Not many subjects were found who had used for such a long-time span, but more than 100 people submitted data on the use of microdosing for more than one week. When it came to periods of 90 days, only three people responded—and these had end of life conditions, e.g. terminal cancer. "Their emotions were all over the place—their standard deviation of emotion was much higher than everyone else's. They also submitted written diary entries, so when I read them, I understood that they were using microdosing to cope with their end of life anxiety, and the emotional swings are better understood that way" (Korb 2018b). These researchers used a psychiatric scale named the Positive and Negative Affect Schedule (PANAS) to evaluate the mood state of their subjects on a daily basis. The results show a lot of mood swings in a moderate range, which are indistinguishable from "usual" mood swings in patients with such grave conditions. However, the results of all three patients show a much greater variation of the mood swings after around 60 days of regular microdosing on every fourth day (Korb 2018a). Korb believes that the longer written reports of some patient groups might be more fruitful to explore possible long-term effects of microdosing than the results of the PANAS scale. From their study's results she concluded "that people's depression and anxiety both improves with microdosing, though people with higher anxiety are likely to have an increase in anxiety in the beginning and drop out" (Korb 2018b). However, there is currently a serious problem when trying to find any extensive descriptions of long-term effects of microdosing in respect to possible betterment of mental health conditions on the internet.

It is worth mentioning, when examining internet accounts, that a certain bias of positive reporting has to be expected. First of all, a lot of people who might have tried microdosing without any effect (and have left microdosing because of that) might not be very keen to post their "findings" on the internet. It has also been shown that scientific studies tend to report more positive than negative results, especially when it comes to "new treatment methods". It is therefore a well-known fact that the effect sizes of new treatment methods, especially in the psychological realm, shrink a lot when more studies on a certain method become available. Two major reasons for this are the decrease in the initial enthusiasm of the researchers and patients and a first round of specific (self-)selected patients, who do not represent the usual or "real" patient population.

Chronic effects of microdosing

Up to now, there are no scientifically valid double-blind and placebo-controlled studies with regard to regular intake of LSD in low doses. The only studies available in respect to long-term daily intake looked for development of tolerance (e.g. Isbell et al. 1955) or investigated treatment of autistic children (e.g. Bender & Sankar 1968). Both kinds of studies used higher doses (100 µg and more), which were taken every day without any gaps. Therefore, one cannot conclude anything relevant for the Fadiman regimen of microdosing from these studies.

It's easy to understand that reliable data about possible effects of microdosing cannot be drawn from uncontrolled experiments by a self-selected group of users (disseminated on the Internet and in booklets). As with other medications, placebo effects are large and cannot be distinguished from "real drug effects". This reservation must be kept in mind when reading extracts from the reports about the effects of regular microdosing which are quoted here. However, some reports are worth mentioning.

In October 2017, a German microdoser had taken 15–25 µg LSD once every 4 days over a period of 10 weeks. The effects were:

> *always the same, with no unusual or incalculable*
> *reactions. ... The effects: there is a slight hyperactivity,*
> *a little increased heartbeat, an extraordinary ability*
> *to concentrate and a drive towards body movement.*
> *It appeared more simple to me to apprehend others,*
> *cognitively and emotionally. I was able to memorize*
> *my past more easily. Dreaming at night wasn't altered.*
> *The state allowed me to solve complex issues with more*
> *ease. Thinking wasn't as broad anymore, what made it*
> *easier to focus on one issue.*
> (Matrixblogger 2017)

In May 2018, researcher Jim Fadiman sent me the following account of a person who has microdosed regularly following the Fadiman protocol (10–20 µg every fourth day). This person reported to him:

- Willingness to do tasks that I hate doing
- Increase in ability to manage my time and sort my tasks.
- Find myself dancing to the music while I work (never used to dance)
- 100% engaged in whatever I'm doing.
- Widened attention: I can pay attention to more than one thing at the same time while still staying on task
- Way less marijuana smoked (lifelong smoker)
- I know when I'm hungry and I eat.
- Same for water intake. I can feel it, I need water. Don't want juice or milk or coffee.
- I have started stretching routines because my body tells me I need it.
- Better conversation ability. I can easily articulate my point.
- Huge decrease in mental chatter through the day, in a mindfulness way.
- Increased alertness to external stimuli and motion, especially in the woods.
- Much better ability to see my system plans in a whole view.
- Able to trust myself.
- Helps with normal anxiety, like going for a job interview or meeting someone new.
- I can deal with asshole people without getting upset.
- Increase in overall enjoyment.

That this user still smoked marijuana produces uncertainty that some of the "symptoms" or "betterments" might in fact have been caused by (albeit to a lesser extent than previously) marijuana smoking. This may also have increased suggestibility. However, these kind of "very positive" reports are rare, even on the internet.

An observational study on microdosers

In a study by Johnstad (2018), twenty-one microdosers were recruited through psychedelic user websites. Most were in their early 30s (students, workers, academics, unemployed). Average duration of experience with psychedelics was 10 years. Thirteen had extensive microdosing experience and eight had experience on a sporadic basis. The study's purpose was to explore how "ordinary" users of psychedelics approach microdosing. Typical questions in the interviews were: Which psychedelics have you microdosed? Do you microdose in cycles or continuously? How often do you do it? What effects do you get from microdosing? Have you noticed any negative effects? Data were analysed using thematic analysis and meaning condensation (Kvale and Brinkmann 2015).

Users without any health issues who felt microdosing helped them usually report that it positively influenced their energy, mood, and cognition and allowed them to function better in everyday life. Some claimed that microdosing increased openness and extraversion and improved their capacity to relate to other people (Johnstad 2018: 45). In respect to pathological conditions, a microdoser reported "I have had very positive results from infrequent psilocybin microdosing. I have found fast and relatively long-lasting relief from depression and social anxiety" (Johnstad 2018: 45). Therapeutic effects were also reported in pain management, obsessive-compulsive disorder (OCD), PTSD, narcolepsy, and migraines. Despite the general emphasis on subtle benign effects, the respondents pointed to some challenges with microdosing. Most commonly reported was overdosing above the microdosing range, which was not regarded as compatible with everyday social activities. Some users reported that microdosing could also exacerbate certain conditions or symptoms. In some cases, felt benign health effects seem to disappear or reverse themselves after longer periods of use. A few respondents also mentioned insomnia, especially if they microdosed late in the day.

6.2 Subjective experiences: Minidosing

A second definition of microdosing is taking a dose which induces some perceptible effects. This means a dose which is above the level of microdosing in the strict sense. The dose range for minidosing is proposed here to be 25–50 µg LSD by mouth. A lot of reports about "microdosing" include definitive perceptible effects of LSD or other psychedelics and might therefore belong to this category.

Experiments around the threshold for minidosing and microdosing

In the first clinical trial with LSD, the psychiatrist Arthur Stoll (1947) found 20 µg to be virtually undetectable, whereas 30 µg produced a few light symptoms, peaking two hours later than with a 100 *µg* dose. Greiner et al. (1958) found reactions in galvanic skin response alterations with doses of 5 *µg* LSD and subjective effects were felt above 20 µg. Canadian psychiatrist Abram Hoffer's subjects did not detect 15 µg, whereas the majority felt 25 µg (Hoffer and Osmond 1967). Test subjects of De Maar et al. (1960) had LSD several times and could identify differences in doses of 25, 50, and 100 µg. In another experiment with 50 µg, most subjects reported slight difficulty in focusing vision, inner trembling, dream-like feeling, weakness, heaviness or lightness of limbs, while other neuropsychological measures were not affected (Abramson et al. 1955).

A study by Greiner et al. (1958) was done with healthy male volunteers, who were given different low doses (4, 7, 20, 40 µg) of LSD by mouth. This experiment was sponsored by the US Army, though it is unclear for what purpose. The experiment was claimed to be double-blind. Subjects were placed in a reclined position in a dark room and a questionnaire was applied at regular intervals. Physiological measures such as the galvanic skin response (GSR) and pupil diameter were also made. Alterations of the GSR were found with the 7 µg dose. Changes in pupil size were not seen with doses lower than 12 µg. Some changes were felt with doses as low as 7 and 12 µg, but consistent perceptible effects have been demonstrated with 20 *µg in respect to* deviations from normal perception of body image, thought and emotion 60–120 minutes post application. With the 20 and 40 µg doses, a dip in alertness and motility at the third hour was followed by a climb above the baseline level for the rest of the day. Control and thought sank gradually for the first three hours, returning to baseline at the fourth hour. Sociability and hedonic tone increased for the first two hours, dipped sharply at the third hour, but remained above baseline for the entire experimental day. However, it was observed that by the third hour, a sudden tiredness with indifference and low mood appeared. No alterations of thought processes were detected. With the 20 µg dose half of the subjects exhibited euphoria, increased psychomotor tension, and distractibility. By the second hour, there was indifference with physical retardation and social withdrawal, irritability and frequent laughter. Changes in thought such as obsessive thinking, and strange and unreal thoughts, were registered. The authors concluded that a threshold dose of 20 µg was confirmed by the experiment. The shifts in mood with the 20 µg dose were not consciously perceived by the subjects, but the authors felt that a lability and shifting in mood was the main consequence of low doses of LSD.

The first study in humans was done with a 30 µg dose

The psychological effects of LSD were discovered by Albert Hofmann in 1943. The first systematic experiments on the drug were carried out in 1946 by Arthur Stoll at the psychiatric hospital of the University of Zurich, Switzerland (Stoll 1947). Probably because of the strong effects that Hofmann experienced in his first self-experiment with a 250 µg dose, Stoll used a dose of only 30 µg. Tests were carried out on a total of 19 healthy individuals under similar conditions. The test conditions allowed for a relaxed state of mind, only minimally influenced by the experimental procedure. Conditions of the experiments were adapted to fit the test subjects' individual needs, in order to obtain as unconstrained an impression of the effects as possible.

Stoll's descriptions of the phenomena observed are very detailed (1947). They were originally given in German and until now have never been presented in translation. A particular value of these first systematic experiments lies in the fact that there was little prior knowledge and relatively few expectations about the experiences induced. If not much is known in advance, specific expectations are minimal and there is likely to be a higher degree of "objectivity" in the reactions. Stoll's test subjects were largely "objective" in this sense and gave direct reports about the symptoms as they occurred. As Stoll's publication provides the best descriptions of the symptoms arising at this dosage level, they are presented here in extensive detail.

The LSD was taken in the morning on an empty stomach. After 30 minutes, a light breakfast was served. The test subjects were then allowed to read, lie down or walk around. The quiet room, with seating and sleeping facilities, was temporarily darkened. The focus was on the psychological observation of the test subjects (in terms of their mood, thoughts, sense of orientation, etc.). In addition, their gait, stance, and speech, tendon reflexes, blood pressure and pulse, and changes to their pupils were investigated. The subjects subsequently produced written reports of what they had experienced.

Chronological sequence: The onset of symptoms consistently occurred after 1.5 hours. After 3 hours, the symptoms peaked. After 5 hours, a noticeable decrease in symptoms was apparent. After a maximum of eight hours, the symptoms had completely disappeared. In many cases, the symptoms came and went in waves, as also noted by some of the test subjects themselves (Diagram 2).

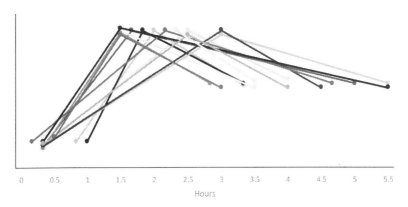

Hours

Diagram 2: Schematic representation of the time course of clinical effects of a dose of 30 µg per os in thirteen different subjects (Stoll 1947)

Motor phenomena: The first effects to occur involved motor disturbances. These predominantly consisted of ataxic symptoms of a sensory nature. These were observed in all test subjects. The subjects took excessively large steps and walked with their legs wide apart, lengthening their stride. The ground felt soft or "slippery" to them. They failed in their attempts to point at things. Sometimes they missed their aim as they tried to grasp things or put them down. In most cases, their speech appeared to be poorly articulated and unclear as they sometimes stumbled over their words. Occasionally, their writing was also erratic and uncertain. There was an increase in the patellar tendon reflexes among some subjects. In some, a finger tremor was observed.

Autonomic symptoms: The intensity and co-occurrence of the symptoms varied significantly. Subjects suffering from autonomic instability tended to react more strongly. A large number of them had a certain feeling of discomfort, slight nausea, or a peculiarly discomfiting sensation of being ill. Some reported pressure in the ears, headache, dizziness or heart palpitations (despite an apparently normal pulse rate). A pale colour was noted on certain subjects' faces. In three test subjects, dilation of the pupils and an impaired pupillary light reflex were observed, along with reports of blurred and fuzzy vision. The subjects experienced ripples of hot and cold, episodes of sweating, and cold hands. In some cases, their breathing became deeper and slower. Blood pressure remained virtually unaffected. When it was affected, it tended to fall rather than rise.

Visual perception: Visual hallucinations were the main phenomena observed. Many subjects noticed extended after-images in the dark. When they closed their eyes, they experienced a wide variety of elementary hallucinations. These ranged from primitive to well-organised images and sequences of images. The hallucinatory images were reported to move. Subjects spoke of random movement, and of flowing, flying and circular patterns. Instances of synaesthesia were repeatedly observed. Most frequently, these were manifested in illusory perceptions of the environment. Regarding pseudo-hallucinations, test subjects were always aware that the phenomena were not real. Some reported excessively clear shapes and edges. People in their familiar surroundings appeared to develop exaggerated physiognomies. When reading, subjects reported seeing letters dance on the page. Mistaken perceptions of perspective were also reported. A tablespoon appeared to be as long as a ladle. The subjects' own hands appeared sometimes large and plump, and at other times distant and small. Colours in the environment looked unusually intense.

Acoustic perception: Approximately 70% of the subjects experienced noises as excessively loud (hyperacusis). For example, a distant clatter sounded like a loud crash. Actual hallucinations of an auditory nature occurred in only very few cases (mostly as a diffuse babble of voices).

Smell and taste: Abnormal perceptions of smell or taste were not reported.

Sense of touch and proprioception: There were repeated reports of a "furry" feeling in the mouth. Some subjects felt a sensation of heaviness, and a laxity and lack of energy in the body. Some had the impression that their head was fatter and their nose was larger. Within the body, a trembling seemed to occur, a strange restlessness.

Thought processes: Subjects' thought processes were almost always altered, predominantly in the sense of feeling more relaxed and moving faster, sometimes accompanied by fleeting ideas, with a broader spectrum of associations following one after the other. On occasion, subjects appeared to lose their train of thought ("I lose track of what I'm thinking"). The subjects felt as if their thoughts were slipping away from them ("I couldn't think right, couldn't think logically"). However, only rarely did subjects report erratic, fragmentary thoughts.

Attention: Sustained attention (tenacity) was reduced and subjects experienced increased absent-mindedness. Over extended periods, the ability of most subjects to form their thoughts seemed to be affected by perseveration.

Mood fluctuations: The test subjects' mood changed on a regular basis (Diagram 3). Generally, there was a feeling of euphoria at the start of the experiment as the subjects started to experience the effects of the substance. In six subjects this persisted, but there was sometimes a swinging back-and-forth into a depressive state. In five cases, the euphoria was manifested as a calm and tranquil sense of serenity, or alternatively as a general feeling of apathy ("I didn't feel at all involved in the things going on around me"). The subjects felt free of worry. A pleasant carefree feeling, without any obligations, with no connections to the past or future ("I was very happy not to be doing anything", "My state of being was dreamlike, so beautiful and pure", "I experienced moments in which I daydreamed about nature, for instance about the flight of birds, with a real childlike joy"). If the outside world (for instance, because of noise) made itself known, it disturbed their contemplations. For other test subjects, the euphoria made them feel more relaxed and happier ("I actually feel a little tipsy"). A spirit of adventure, walking around ostentatiously, and a domineering attitude were observed. Not infrequently there was an unmotivated giggle, which could turn into an urge to laugh. Commonplace utterances or situations provoked laughter, though the subjects knew that the situation was not actually funny. In one case, there was also a long-lasting fragility of mood, in which the subject was torn between laughing and crying. There were also fluctuations of a depressive nature, a quiet sadness or mellow sentimentality. In four subjects there were noticeable hints of a suicidal feeling.

A: Pure Euphoria

B: Euphoria then Depression

C: Depression then Euphoria

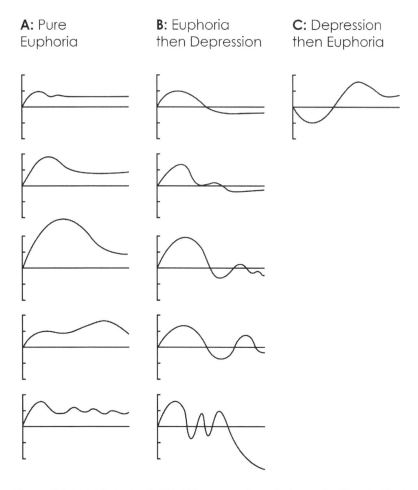

Diagram 3: Schematic representations of the course of moods changes in different subjects with 30 µg LSD (Stoll 1947)

Sexuality: No subjects gave an impression of eroticisation.

Awareness levels, experience of time, self-evaluation, and sense of self: Awareness levels seemed to be impaired. Some subjects experienced a mild but distinct feeling of light-headedness. In no instances was the sense of locational or situational orientation affected. Subjects were always aware of their situation. Time was experienced sometimes as moving more slowly than normal, sometimes as moving faster, or even as having stopped. Subjects always retained a capacity for self-evaluation. In half of the cases, however, an "ambivalent uninhibitedness" was observed, a compulsion to express thoughts that the subjects actually wanted to suppress.

Changes in the subjects' sense of self: Subjects sometimes reported a feeling of distance, a lack of connection, and a sense of alienation from themselves and from the world ("I'm not quite here", "It's strange, as if I'm no longer myself", "I'm standing next to me and looking at myself"). From time to time, a sense of fear arose and in five cases a slightly paranoid feeling.

After-effects: The after-effects were characterised both by symptoms that had already occurred during the experiment and by secondary reactions to the preceding intoxication. These included a continuing absent-mindedness (e.g. mistyping on the typewriter). Several test subjects were euphoric and experienced a new-found appreciation of their usual surroundings ("I feel young and beautiful and fresh." "It's like I've just been born"). Subjects took ownership of familiar things at home again, as if they were gifts. They responded to music with much more feeling than usual. Most of the subjects were very tired following the intoxication and slept deeply and for longer than normal. The next day was characterised partly by a normal feeling of freshness for work but also by a hangover-like feeling, involving headache, pain in the limbs and low spirits. Repeatedly the next morning, faulty memory function was observed. Subjects had to write down planned activities.

Stoll's descriptions from these early experiments give the most comprehensive description of the effects of low-dose LSD and its after-effects ever written. Because all other descriptions from very early LSD research are considerably shorter and much more fragmented, they are not included here.

Two scientific experiments with minidoses of LSD

Gastaut et al. (1953) did an unblinded observational study on 12 healthy volunteers with 40–60 µg LSD. Responses were classified as autonomic, psychic, and electroencephalographic. "In 4 instances only one or two of these responses were observed, while in 7 cases all three responses were elicited. In one case LSD had no effect" (Gastaut et al. 1953: 119). Affect became labile with a tendency to euphoria. Hyperactivity and instability of the autonomic nervous system was obvious in most subjects. All subjects experienced a decrease in intellectual capabilities. Psychological tests (Cattell, Rorschach, Lahy) revealed that attention and abstract thinking were impaired. Notably, this was in contrast to the subjective impression of the subjects who felt enhanced vitality and efficacy.

Abramson et al. (1955d) tested arithmetic performance, using simple combinations of addition and subtraction problems. Performance at doses of

50 µg and 100 µg LSD was significantly worse than placebo. Interestingly, learning and practice effects seem to disappear under the drug's influence, which points to disturbed learning processes.

In a double-blind experiment using 20 µg LSD by Vojtechovsky et al. (1972) in twelve healthy students, the unexperienced subjects were paired and received either LSD-placebo, LSD-LSD, or placebo-placebo. Social performance was observed in the laboratory and while performing social contacts in town. The most frequent symptoms were euphoria and unmotivated smiling. All symptoms could be significantly better controlled while in town than in the laboratory. No unusual behaviour emerged under the stress of social tasks.

Minidosing experiment with a verified dose

What follows is the description of a subjective experience following the ingestion of 37.5 µg LSD by mouth. The subject of this experiment was a 50-year-old scientist, an experienced LSD user, who did the experiment in 2018. Identity and amount of the LSD were verified toxicologically.

> *1:05pm. Ingestion of 37.5 µg LSD by mouth.*
> *2:20pm. Nothing felt*
> *2:25pm. Poor vision (visual accommodation). Mild mental irritation. Greater effort needed to concentrate. Thinking becomes more difficult, and it takes more effort not to lose the thread.*
> *2:50pm. Slight intensification of the above effects. Mood generally very slightly dysphoric.*
> *4:25pm. Mental irritation and concentration difficulties more pronounced. Distinct effects can be felt. Empty feeling in the stomach. Even eating something helped only a little. A queasy feeling persisted for several hours. Blurred vision slightly less pronounced (adaptation?) but was still present.*
> *4:40pm. I went out as mental irritation so pronounced that no further clerical work was possible; also a sense of not wanting to do this any longer; a kind of "so what?" feeling. Once outside, a sense of detachment. A tendency not to want to concentrate, even when reading the names of plants in the botanical garden. There was no increased openness to sensory stimuli; on the contrary, a*

feeling of emotional numbness and a somewhat fuzzy perception of things. Slight feeling of discomfort. No euphoria or if present, only very weak and mixed (with dysphoria at the same time). A continued feeling of queasiness in the stomach.

At around 5:30pm, a tangible weakening of the effects. Still a slight underlying sense of the effects, sometimes noticeable in communication. For others, however—if they were asked—this was no longer noticeable during the phone call, although the effects after 1.5–3.5 hours were clearly still perceptible in communication and were described in terms of slightly slower and slurred speech. Felt hungry and at around 6:00pm and went out to eat (fish soup) at the train station, which was very crowded (after a football game). But only mild impairment; things felt okay there.

At around 7:30pm, hardly any perceptible remaining effects.

At 8:00pm, still only slightly noticeable underlying effects. Possibly a slightly greater urge to be active than normal. Still no inclination at this point to fall into my relaxing evening routine (Saturday). Therefore did a little tidying.

At 8:45pm, still a mild underlying effect apparent.

During a spontaneous telephone conversation at about 9:00pm, certain concentration problems were still evident throughout, causing me to lose the thread of my thoughts. Became aware, however, only when someone called.

At 10:30pm, still a mildly perceptible effect, with a low ability to concentrate or a noticeable effect on concentration. Multiplication (maths) was difficult. Reading is okay, however, and understanding too. Perhaps a tad harder than normal.

Later in the evening, found the "Soft Parade" album by The Doors again and danced to it for almost an hour. Slept without problems. Synopsis: Overall, no optical effects observed apart from detachment and indistinct vision. No thought disorders in the true sense of the term, but rather normal thought processes. These could be controlled, however, only with greater effort than usual; also, sometimes a tendency to lose the thread; in the evening, too, thinking remained more difficult than normal to a small yet perceptible degree. In terms of communication, others noticed a difference. Mood definitely not euphoric, but also not really dysphoric; somewhat detached, even autistic feelings, more distant from surroundings, at least to some degree. No particular feeling of intensification or liveliness or of having more ideas, for example. Rather a feeling of being impaired. Then, in the evening, a perhaps more relaxed, easy-going mood.

The first self-reports of physicians in 1948

Prior to a series of experiments conducted by Condrau (1949) on mentally ill patients, trials were carried out on some healthy subjects to learn further about LSD's effects and to compare the experiences of healthy volunteers to those of the mentally ill. The healthy volunteers were mainly doctors. Since the test subjects had very little information about the effects of the substance, they were able to give reports about their experiences without much influence from prior expectations. The descriptions were given by introspective subjects, are unusually detailed and well written. It appears worth recounting three of these reports to learn about subjective effects of LSD in the 20–40 µg range.

> **Record 1** (physician, 20 µg per os): The eagerness to work suddenly dissipated; I walked around the office the whole time without doing even the slightest thing. I would not even have been capable of writing a letter. Nonetheless, I found that I was in a very active state internally: my awareness of my inability to do anything did not bother me in the slightest. I viewed this as quite normal. In addition, I had an almost paranoid attitude to the world around me. I felt that everyone was looking at me unusually sharply, observing me and apparently viewing me as somehow changed... I also found it extremely silly that I could not stop laughing. To this was added my subjective perception of heaviness in the limbs as well as symptoms of ataxia. I had the feeling that if someone were to touch me or gently nudge me, I would fall over... I did not notice an actual stumbling over my words but did experience signs of difficulty in speaking. My tongue sometimes felt a little clumsy; I would, for example, hardly have been able to deliver an extended speech. My writing was not altered, though I had a slight subjective feeling of uncertainty when writing... There was also

a strong urge to communicate, sometimes even a constant need to talk. During the concentration test, however, I had the feeling of a significantly weakened ability to concentrate. Thus, all kinds of thoughts went through my head that I simply could not dispel. (Condrau 1949: 15/16)

Record 2 (physician, 40 μg LSD per os): About one hour after taking the dose, a general feeling of hotness came over me, which slowly increased until I started to sweat... at the same time, I felt less and less able to concentrate. It took me about a quarter of an hour to look for and locate two telephone numbers in the directory. My interest in clerical tasks vanished completely. I noted an increasing motor agitation, which was expressed in an urge to keep busy and that made me wander around the office continuously, moving objects and files on the table, and occasionally leafing through a patient's medical history but without the slightest ability to concentrate. This state was associated with a subjective feeling of pronounced euphoria and seemed very natural to me. I felt light, almost floating, and thought neither of the past nor of the future... It was actually a manic presentation. In the room, I pulled out the telephone cord so as not to be disturbed in this blissful state and lay down on the bed. The urge to keep busy immediately caused me to walk around the room again, and I left a lighted cigarette untouched and browsed through a book of artworks instead, and then half-ate some pears and could not stop continually laughing. I started to drum on the top of the desk, an activity that evoked further irresistible laughter from me. It seemed to me now as if all those present were staring at me with big, dark eyes. When a brass lizard was extended towards me, I recoiled because it suddenly appeared alive to me... A freshly waxed parquet floor suddenly looked as if it were cloaked in an intense orange colour. At one point I felt sharp pain in my calves and had the feeling that I could suffer cramp there at any moment. I sat down on the floor and wriggled my legs, laughing. In the dark room, distinct optical hallucinations appeared of an elementary kind. An infinite number of bright points were moving wildly through one another... I was not remotely surprised but saw these phenomena

as normal and watched them in what was even a self-absorbed and amused way... At around 12:00 noon, my manic state started to slowly dissipate and gave way to quite another feeling. Most prominently, this involved a loss of contact with my surroundings. While I could register everything, I was quite unable to establish an affective relationship with my environment. In an autistically self-contained state, I seemed to be moving within it as if in a viscous mass. My cognitive and motor processes were slowed down significantly. Everything seemed like an indescribable effort and generated a feeling of helplessness that was, however, not altogether unpleasant. In the evening I could hardly sleep in spite of a strong sense of fatigue, as I reinterpreted various night-time noises in illusory terms and was startled every time.
(Condrau1949: 17)

Record 3 (physician, 40 μg LSD per os): It feels as if my body is lighter than usual. While walking up the stairs to the doctors' office, I have a subjective feeling that I am a little unsteady on my feet, as if slightly tipsy. Only with difficulty can I suppress a quite unwarranted smile. In the doctors' office, where I have my pigeonhole, everything looks unchanged but nonetheless somewhat distant and alien. I have to reread some sentences three or four times and even then cannot understand them. On some occasions, the ability to concentrate returns for a few minutes but only if I make a conscious effort. However, such moments, in which I can almost completely understand what I am reading, become shorter and shorter. The letters begin to change so that certain words, which I in some way feel are more important than the others, look a little larger. The article, written by a philosopher, eventually feels like empty blather despite the fact that I simultaneously have a very clear awareness that it is, of course, nothing of the kind. Curiously, however, this ambivalence does not disconcert me in the least; I place the volume down and sit for approximately one minute somewhat lethargically at the table. On standing up, I am surprised to experience a pronounced feeling of physical lightness, almost as if I could float. I feel a pleasant warmth spread from my back across my entire skin... The feeling of tension in my head...

and my whole body has increased considerably. I feel the urge to dance and feel so light that I do so on my own in the room for a few minutes. Then, I lie down on the sofa, thinking of nothing and feeling pleasantly warm all over. But then I suddenly feel a cold shiver down my back and soon feel really freezing; in response, I quickly get up and put on a sweater. When writing, [I] also [experience] mild coordination difficulties, which also affect my speech... My hands feel cold and damp. I feel a certain nausea though no urge to vomit. I have the impression that my emotions have become quite flat, yet react very quickly. Time seems to pass more quickly than in the past. I feel like I no longer have any accurate sense of the passing of time. I experience some contact difficulties and manage only with effort to express myself clearly to some degree, as the terms melt away from me, just as the words disappear. I still maintain, however, that in my current state I could empathise with any possible state of mind experienced by other people. I have the repeated feeling that I am actually only spouting twaddle... and then cannot help suddenly laughing because of this—something I usually find quite unpleasant. I feel a little humiliated that the LSD has changed me in this way. I feel significantly altered, in the sense of being a caricature of my other character traits. When I want to leave the villa for lunch, it occurs to me that I have forgotten the front-door key. No sooner have I fetched it than I discover instead... that I don't have my fountain pen with me... While walking, the strange floating feeling returns. I suddenly have the sensation of having very tiny legs, but even so continue to take steps of a normal length. In front of the casino, I meet a local pastor and have the impression that he can clearly see that there is something not quite right about me. My colleagues— male and female—have a rigid, or robotic, quality about them. From time to time, I am struck by an irresistible urge to laugh despite the fact that I am actually not in a laughing mood at all... I often make quite ridiculous remarks. I am no longer capable of clearly thinking about more complex connections. All sorts of incoherent, strange thoughts follow one after the other but are so vague, almost dream-like, that I cannot retain them. The face of a colleague looks very broad to me, changing rapidly, and then quite thin again; also, both halves of his face seem to change independently of one another. My passive distractibility level has increased dramatically. First here, then there, I catch a word from other people's conversations, try to hook on to it, but my thought process fails to get into gear... I have the clear impression that everyone who comes within a few metres of me is looking at me probingly, a situation I do not find very pleasant. My movements look very angular to me. People have a kind of lifeless, puppet-like, mask-like, artificial quality. Certain details in their behaviour look ridiculous, insincere, like actors but ones performing badly. I find it partly funny yet partly worrying that people clearly fail to notice that I am no longer fully normal. Like an 'epiphany', it strikes me that it fundamentally doesn't matter what we do, as we cannot change the way the world works.

(Condrau 1949: 20/21).

In sum, the preceding descriptions and reports show that doses in the 20–50 µg range reliably induce a spectrum of mild subjective effects in humans. As Stoll (1947) and the description of the subjects of Condrau (1949) illustrate, these effects cover a lot of psychological and cognitive functions. Mood seems to be especially affected, in several respects: 1. The mood felt is accentuated; 2. the variability of mood is greater, 3. the lability of mood in increased. Subjective changes can be controlled somewhat within this dose range, but the whole person seems to be affected by the changes. In virtually all cases the subjects reported distraction, induced by the effects of the drug. They felt subjective performance deficits and "irritations" caused by the drug. It also appears obvious that distractions in everyday performance were felt by most subjects. Some reported a specific kind of "detachment" from themselves and the environment, often associated with less focus and difficulty in following an intended chain of actions. It is clear from the descriptions that minidoses irritate the cognitive system by affecting many of its functions. This can be dysfunctional in most everyday circumstances, as the descriptions of Condrau (1949) show, but might have other applications if used under certain conditions, e.g. when playing music or performing painting.

7

Scientific Studies of Low-Dose LSD

In the following pages, I will present all the scientific format studies which were conducted and documented with low doses of LSD in the range of 5–50 µg. In all experiments, the drug was given by mouth as the tartrate salt (unless described otherwise). First, the uncontrolled observational studies will be briefly described and then the controlled clinical studies will be presented. Thereafter, studies on pathological conditions such as depression, anxiety, obsessive-compulsive neurosis, cephalalgias and others will be presented. Finally, I will report on studies on other issues such as sleep and dreaming. The presentation follows a chronological order in each subchapter.

7.1 Effects of low-dose LSD on healthy subjects

Observational studies

Observational studies are those in which an experimental subject receives a drug without any objective measures being taken. Usually an outside observer is present to register the observable effects. The experimental subject is generally a healthy volunteer given the task of reporting subjective effects of the drug. Observational studies have the advantage that the drug's effects can be observed without predetermining what to measure, which is of particular advantage when the drug's effects are not known. Observational studies are able to provide some initial data as well as observations on the effects of the drug and bring to attention any possible hindrances for scientific studies or dangers that would have to be taken into account with any quantitative studies, which usually follow the initial observational studies.

The first clinical study on LSD effects on normal subjects was conducted at the Zürich University Psychiatric Clinic, 75 miles away from the laboratory of the Swiss pharmaceutical company Sandoz in Basel, where Albert Hofmann discovered LSD's psychoactive effects in 1943. Psychiatrist Werner A. Stoll conducted the first clinical study, an observational study published in 1947. The purpose of the study was to explore the subjective effects of LSD on normal subjects under almost free conditions, i.e. no restrictions or experimental procedures with which the subjects had to comply. Stoll observed behavioural changes as well as the subjective reports given by the subjects whilst experiencing the acute effects. The subjects were also asked to write a retrospective protocol. Interestingly, the study was conducted with a dose of 30 µg, presumably because of the "psychotic trip", which Hofmann had reported from his first intentional self-experiment with a dose of 250 µg. With respect to the results, which still represent the most detailed account of the effects of LSD in the low dose range, I refer the reader to Chapter 7.1, where they are described in detail.

In the same clinical environment in Zürich, psychiatrist Gion Condrau (1949) conducted 130 LSD sessions in the framework of a clinical observational study, which again used no objective measurements. Subjects were dosed daily for six to ten days. On the first days, 20–40 µg was administered per os and the dose increased over the following days. There were also experiments where the doses were given every other day. Other subjects received decreasing doses during the course of the six to ten days. The publication presents some extensive case vignettes that describe a clinical picture of the LSD effects. Condrau states that two experiments with 30 µg did not show any effects, whereas 40 µg led to distinct effects. Some of the very detailed descriptions of subjective effects are presented in Chapter 6.

In another observational study, Becker (1949) tried to evaluate psychopathological symptoms induced by LSD. Nineteen healthy physicians received LSD (30–40 µg) in 24 experiments. Seven subjects received 30 µg: three subjects experienced "no effect", whilst in the remaining four only slight effects were observed. Fourteen subjects received 40 µg: one subject experienced "no effects", three felt slight effects, and ten exhibited signs of a marked "intoxication". According to the author, symptoms varied greatly and were dependent on the subject's personality. With respect to side effects, a prolonged effect was observed in seven cases, particularly notable in the spheres of affect, impulsivity and contact.

In a psychopathological study, Weyl (1951) conducted 32 experiments on twenty-seven healthy subjects (seven females, twenty males, age range 22–35 years). It was a non-blind observational study. The experimenters tried to provide the subjects with as much freedom as possible to choose their preferred activity. In five pilot experiments the volunteers were dosed with 30 µg LSD, but did not report any symptoms. This contrasted with doses of 60 µg, where all subjects showed significant psychopathological symptoms.

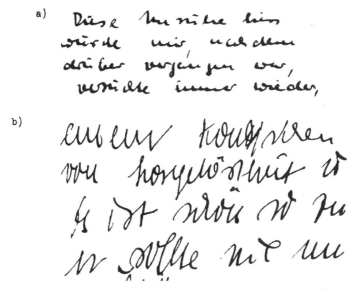

Figure 3: Handwriting under the influence of no drug (top) and changes after 60 µg LSD (Weyl 1951).

In 1951, Rinkel et al. gave doses of 20–90 µg LSD to normal subjects and mentally ill patients in an observational study to look for "schizophrenia-like symptoms". They found some of the expected symptoms with the higher doses, but no precise results from the different doses were given.

Delay and Pichot (1951) report very briefly on some "initial" uncontrolled experiments with low doses of LSD (20–60 µg) and recount that they were able to detect some symptoms (euphoria, humour, depressive and anxious moods, intellectual modifications, and visual illusions).

Forrer and Goldner (1951) report on their observations during 42 "treatments" of six male schizophrenic patients with doses of 0.5, 1, 2, 4, and 6 µg/kg LSD. With 0.5 µg LSD/kg, five out of six patients noted definite changes, which peaked at 2–2.5 hours, subsiding after 5–5.5 hours. Euphoria, increased talkativeness, and outbursts of laughter were noted. No data were given on the different doses. However, they found that pupil size was related to dose and peak effects and occurred at two to three hours after administration. Blood sugar levels slightly raised 2–3 hours after LSD and a significant leukocytosis was found with doses above 1 μg/kg. In conclusion, the authors "... believe that the increase in accessibility and spontaneity as a result of administration of lysergic acid diethylamide is a general reaction phenomenon ..." (p. 586).

Arnold and Hoff (1953) observed the effects of LSD in a non-controlled, non-blinded study (50, 80, 120 μg) on psychopathological symptoms. A table of symptoms and clinical observations was used to assess the effects. Nineteen normal subjects (and some severely ill patients) were studied, but no differential data were presented. With a dose of 50 μg "virtually nothing" was observed in respect to symptoms, whereas 80 and 120 μg led to significant symptoms.

Gastaut et al. (1953) reported an unblinded observational study on twelve healthy normal subjects with 40–60 μg LSD. Baseline measures were recorded before the LSD was given. Responses of the subjects were classified as autonomic, psychic and electroencephalographic. "In four instances only one or two of these responses were observed, while in seven cases all three responses were elicited."

All subjects experienced a decrease in intellectual capabilities. Psychological tests (Cattell, Rorschach, Lahy) revealed that attention and abstract thinking were impaired. This was in contrast to the subjective impression of the subjects, who felt enhanced vitality and efficacy. Affect became labile with a tendency to euphoria. Hyperactivity and instability of the autonomic nervous system was obvious in most subjects. In the EEG, the alpha-rhythm was increased (0.5–4.0 cycles per second). In half of the cases a central beta-rhythm was initiated or accentuated. Stimulation by flickering light caused an increase in occipital potentials in seven instances, and an irradiation of the frontal regions occurred in five cases.

Gamma et al. (1954) report extensively on four self-experiments with doses of 20 and 50 μg of LSD. The self-experiments led to many slight changes in psychological functions. A blood cell count of the experimenter was conducted and showed a 30% increase of leucocyte cells after 20 μg (40% with 50 μg). However, this might be an unspecific stress response. No other types of blood cells showed any alteration.

Anderson and Rawnsley (1954) did an observational study with four normal subjects and nineteen mentally ill patients. A wide range of dosages (10–600 µg) was administered. Some subjects were dosed over a few days. Unfortunately, the results section does not present data separately on normal subjects and patients, nor the different doses. In one normal subject, a "mild stimulation" was reported with a 40 µg dose and a "feeling of impending ego-dissolution" in two normal subjects given 50 µg (p. 44/45). However, most experiments were done with doses much higher than 50 µg.

Savage (1952) reported an observational study with LSD in the range of 10–100 µg. Unfortunately, no exact data on different doses were given and no quantitative measures were used. According to the author, low-dose LSD produced elation, depression and anxiety and a "regression to an autistic state" and alterations in "ego-feeling", including depersonalization. According to the author's observations, "in some instances these effects could be induced by doses as low as 10 micrograms" (Savage 1952: 1).

Pierce (1961) did self-experiments with LSD to explore whether premedication with the antihistamine drug hydroxyzine (Atarax®) would change LSD's effects. Doses of 40, 80, and 130 µg were administered orally after premedication with five doses of 25 mg hydroxyzine or placebo on the previous day. To objectify the effects, the Kraepelin test, the draw-a-tree test, and the Rorschach test were used. Blood pressure, pulse rate, pupil diameter and EEG parameters should have indicated physical effects. However, even with the placebo premedication the author did not perceive any reaction after 40 and 80 µg, which the author interpreted as "a very high tolerance to LSD".

Controlled clinical studies

One of the most prominent LSD researchers in the 1950s and 1960s was Harold Abramson at the New York Mount Sinai Hospital. Abramson cooperated closely with the CIA and the US Army and his major research projects were financed by organizations which were covers for funneling money from military sources, e.g. the Geschickter Fund for Medical Research (cf. Scheflin & Opton 1978). However, Abramson also participated in therapeutic work with LSD and organized two major conferences on the subject of LSD in psychotherapy (Abramson 1960, 1967). Preceding this interest, Abramson conducted studies on the neurocognitive measures and other parameters in dose-response studies using a sound scientific design.

The first study of Abramson et al. (1955e) used 26 healthy volunteers (15 males, 11 females, age 24–41 years, IQ range 100–137). The 48 experiments (13 x placebo, 21 x 25–75 µg (mostly 50 µg), 14 x 100–225 µg) were performed single-blind. The 47-item questionnaire for LSD symptoms was developed by the researchers through the evaluation of the literature. Items were related to physiological and perceptual symptoms. Experiments were performed in groups of 2–4 subjects. Subjects received the drug in the morning after a light breakfast. Measurements with the questionnaire were conducted every hour to establish the course of symptoms. Examples for items related to physiological reactions were: "Is your appetite decreased? Does your head ache? Are your palms moist? Do you feel drowsy?". The authors used LSD doses, mostly in the 50–225 µg range. Unfortunately, it is not detailed in this publication how many subjects received the 25–75 µg dose. A general conclusion drawn from the data is that the symptom questionnaire showed no significant difference between the 25–75 µg and the 100–225 µg dose.

The authors were astonished by how many of their subjects reacted strongly to placebo. One subject reacted positively to more than half of the questionnaire items over a 10-hour period. It appeared obvious to the authors that previous studies reporting on the effects of LSD-25 on normal subjects needed re-evaluation in terms of placebo reactions. "… It was found by us that for a given group of individuals suitable evaluation of responses to LSD-25 could not be made without the use of a zero-dose control group" (Abramson et al. 1955e: 8).

As part of the study by Abramson et al. (1955g) above, the Bender-Gestalt Test (Bender 1946) was repeatedly administered to several subjects in the same room at the same time. Tests were conducted after placebo, 50 µg, and 100 µg. Most of the subjects (13 females, 13 males, 22–39 years) were students who spent the day at the experimental laboratory, either alone or in groups of from three to six. The hypothesis was that normal subjects under LSD will copy the designs of the Bender-Gestalt Test in a manner resembling that of psychiatric patients, and that their deviation scores will increase with increasing dosage of the drug. Various comparisons reveal that the mean scores of experimental subjects given 50 and 100 µg LSD changed in a direction resembling more closely the scores of psychiatric patients, but results were not significant when compared to placebo (Abramson et al. 1955g).

In another experiment, Abramson et al. (1955f) tested 31 healthy volunteers with "superior intelligence" at six dose levels of LSD: zero, 1–25 µg, 26–50 µg, 51–75 µg, 76–100 µg, and 101+ µg. The testing was the measurement of clinical reactions, i.e. how the subjects behaved and what they reported in respect to their "subjective reactions". The authors grouped their data into "selected descriptive parameters" or clusters of symptoms (Abramson et al. 1955f):

- *Euphoria:*(a) fatuousness, (b) laughter, (c) elation
- *Dysphoria*: (a) depression, (b) feelings of sadness
- *Distortions of perception*: (a) auditory, (b) visual, (c) taste, (d) time
- *Neurotic*: (a) nervousness, (b) anxiety, (c) inner trembling, (d) sweating, (e) moist palms, (f) palpitations-tachycardia, (g) difficulty in breathing, (h) trembling, (i) increased pulse rate, (j) feelings of hotness   or coldness, (k) polyuria
- *Psychotic:* (a) hallucinations, (b) delusions, (c) depersonalization, (d) illusions, (e) dream-like feelings, (f) feelings of strangeness, (g) confusion, (h) suspiciousness, (i) uncommunicativeness

The results given in Table 3 indicate that as the dose increases, more subjects report psychotic-like phenomena and distortions of perception. However, there is no positive relationship between dose and neurotic signs.

Number of subjects		20	8	25	10	15	6
Dose (µg LSD)	Zero	1–25	26–50	51–75	76–100	101+	
Psychotic		0.05	0.11	0.60	0.71	1.03	1.11
Distortions in perception		0.45	0.31	0.98	0.71	1.42	1.88
Neurotic		1.68	2.55	2.55	2.46	2.87	3.00

Table 3: The mean number of signs for each of three parameters at each dose level (Abramson et al. (1955f).

The authors conclude, that "since numbers of neurotic signs reported at zero micrograms is comparatively high and there is little correlation between neurotic signs and dose, it is suggested that the neurotic signs are not as much a function of the situation and [more a function of] the personality of the subjects" (Abramson 1955f: 58).

Some substudies of Abramson's group were done within the same experiment, but published separately. Therefore, a synoptic outline about subjects and the experimental procedure is given here. Twelve healthy volunteers (2 females, 6 males, 21–33 years, normal to superior intelligence) were recruited for the study. Subjects were dosed with zero (placebo), 50 µg, or 100 µg LSD in this partially double-blind experiment.

In the first experiment all subjects received a zero dose (i.e. placebo), the second time 50 µg, and the third time 100 µg. In order to measure the effect of repeated testing (learning and practice factor) all subjects received a zero dose on the fourth experimental day. In the following paragraphs an overview on measures and results of the different substudies is provided. The studies focus on different measures of neuropsychological performance.

In one substudy, Jarvik et al. (1955a) used cancellation tests to determine the effects of LSD on indices of attention and concentration. A cancellation test is one in which the subject underlines or crosses out certain recurring items or classes of items on a page of repetitive, though randomized material. Accuracy and speed are measured. Tests were administered 75–90 minutes after drug ingestion. Two types of tests were used: those requiring simple discrimination and those requiring complex discrimination. As shown in Diagrams 4 and 5, the 50 µg dose did virtually nothing, but a significant difference was demonstrated with the 100 µg dose. In the complex discrimination tasks, the 50 µg group showed better performance than with placebo, which might point to practice effects from the first experiment (placebo). Interestingly, no decrease was found with the 50 µg dose in the complex discrimination tasks. However, the 100 µg dose group showed a significant decrease in performance as compared to placebo. Spearman rank correlation coefficients indicated a significant difference in the 50 µg group compared to placebo in three of the simple discrimination tasks and in one of complex discrimination tasks.

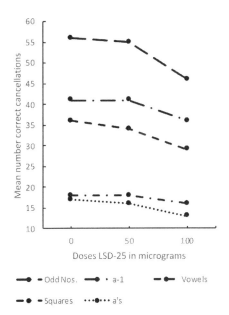

Diagram 4: Mean scores of five cancellation tests involving simple discrimination under two doses of LSD (Jarvik et al. 1955a)

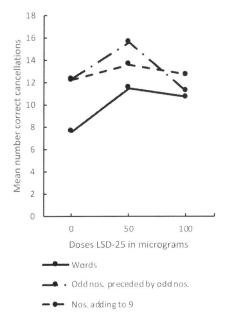

Diagram 5: Mean scores of three cancellation tests involving complex discrimination under two doses of LSD (Jarvik et al. 1955a)

Jarvik et al. (1955b) also investigated the effects upon recall and recognition of various stimuli. Five visual and four auditory tests were used, presenting stimuli of varying degrees of familiarity. Tests were done one hour after drug ingestion. Visual stimuli were projected on a screen from a slide projector. The subjects were asked after specific time intervals to memorize the items shown before. The auditory tests were presented verbally by the experimenter, including digit span, sentence recall, unrelated word recall, and paired associate word recall. As can be seen in Diagrams 6 and 7, for the most part, the scores decreased from the pre-LSD session compared to 50 µg, and decreased even more with 100 µg. An exception was the word opposite test where there was a slight increase from placebo to the 50 µg score, which might represent a practice effect. In general, the highest scores were obtained on the recognition tests, and the lowest on the recall of intense syllables. Few changes were significant, and occurred only in the 100 µg group (except one). Only the decrease on the visual object recall task reached statistical significance within the 50 µg group. There were few significant differences between the 50 µg and the 100 µg groups, which points to a decrease in performance in the 50 µg group. In sum, 50 µg produced a slight decrease in performance with recall and recognition tasks.

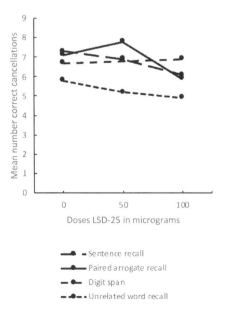

Diagram 6: Mean number of correct memories on five auditory recall and recognition tests under two doses of LSD (Jarvik et al. 1955b)

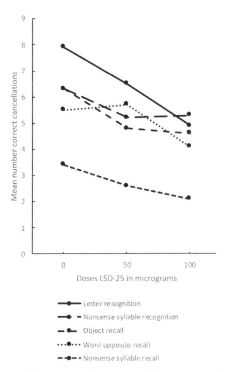

Diagram 7: Mean number of correct memories on five visual recall and recognition tests under two doses of LSD (Jarvik et al. 1955b)

In the same experiment, Abramson et al. (1955a) used the Pursuit Rotor Test (PST) and the Dunlop Steadiness Test (DST) to measure psychomotor performance and hand-eye coordination (Diagrams 8 to 10). The PST consists of a phonograph turntable, which rotates at either 33 and 78 revolutions per minute. There is a round copper button, 8 mm in diameter, situated 7.5 cm from the centre of the turntable. The subject has to follow this button with another button 8 mm in diameter, at the end of the moveable arm of a hinged stylus 25 cm in length. The longer the time in contact, the better the performance. The DST consisted of a copper plate with two holes, 8 mm and 4 mm in diameter. The subject has to hold the wooden handle of a steel stylus, 23 cm in length and 2.5 mm in diameter, and keep this in contact with the edge of the holes. For the PST test, the time in contact with the button and the number of contacts was recorded during five 10-second intervals. Eight of twelve subjects were tested 120–150 minutes after drug ingestion. Diagram 9 show the mean number of seconds (out of 50 seconds) in which the subjects were in contact with the copper button on the PST. At 33 rpm contact time remained the same with a dose of 50 µg and placebo, but dropped slightly at 100 µg. At 78 rpm the contact time dropped insignificantly with 50 µg, but increased significantly with 100 µg. On the DST the time of contact with the sides of the large and small holes is shown in Diagram 10. The time in contact increased with dose, but no change was significant. With Spearman rank correlations a significant difference can be demonstrated between the placebo and 50 µg group on the PRT at 78 rpm and in the steadiness test with respect to number of contacts with the large hole. Results on the two tests of steadiness are similar to the pursuit rotor findings. The practice effect leads one to expect improvement on trials subsequent to the first (drug-free) trial. Since the opposite phenomenon occurred, it can be said that LSD makes people unsteady and prevents them from improving with practice.

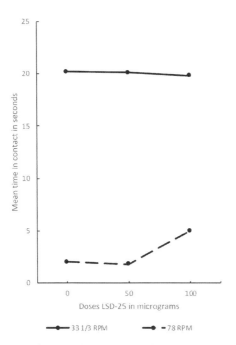

Diagram 8: Mean time in contact, in a 50-second period, with rotating button (Abramson et al. 1955a)

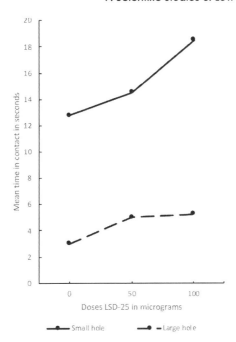

Diagram 9: Mean time in contact, in a 50-second period, with the sides of a large and small hole (Abramson et al. 1955a)

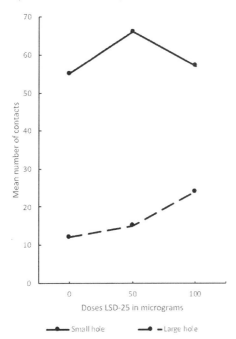

Diagram 10: Mean number of contacts, in a 50-second period, with the sides of a large and small hole (Abramson et al. 1955a)

In another substudy within the same experiment, Jarvik et al. (1955c) investigated arithmetic test performance, using simple combinations of addition and subtraction problems. Tests were done 60–150 minutes after drug ingestion. Arithmetic problems were given on paper sheets. Performance at doses of 50 µg and 100 µg of LSD was significantly lower than placebo. Decreases appear to be even more marked when learning and practice effects are considered, which seem to disappear under the drug's influence (Diagrams 11 and 12). Some complexities of the tests should be mentioned. The solution of simple arithmetic problems demands the ability to do abstract thinking, to concentrate and shut out distractions, and to recall numbers. However, there were no significant differences in the number of errors made under both doses of LSD; the lower performance was much more dependent on the time taken to solve the problems. According to the authors, arithmetic tests are relatively sensitive for detecting LSD effects.

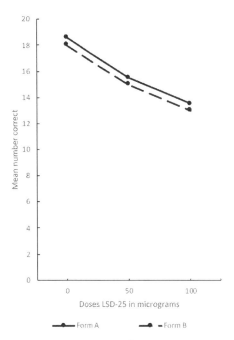

Diagram 11: Mean number of correct solutions of simple arithmetic problems by twelve subjects under two doses of LSD (Jarvik et al. 1955c)

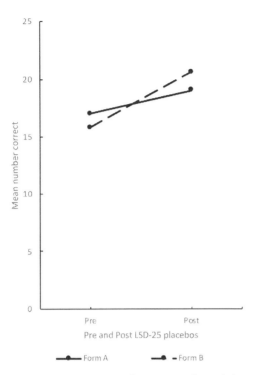

Diagram 12: Mean number of correct solutions of simple arithmetic problems by eight subjects tested under zero dose LSD before drug tests and after drug tests (to illustrate learning and practice effects) (Jarvik et al. 1955c)

Two tests were applied for possible alterations in the perception of spatial relations as a neurocognitive measure (Abramson 1955c). The Thurston Hand Test (THT) was devised by LL Thurstone in 1925. It consists of 49 drawings of right and left hands in various positions. The subject has to indicate whether each drawing represents the right or left hand. The second test of spatial relations was the Minnesota Paper Form Board Test (MPFBT) prepared by Likert and Quasha. It consists of problems in which a geometrical figure is broken into parts. The subject has to select, from five complete geometric figures, the one which represents the parts correctly fitted together. The tests were conducted at 50 and 100 μg LSD, and zero doses. The results show that LSD tends to impair the subject's scores on tests of spatial relations, but with the 50 μg dose no statistically significant change was detected, while 100 μg significantly decreased performance on the THT. On the MPFB the only significant change was between the two drug doses.

In the same experiment, Abramson et al. (1955b) conducted reaction time tests. The manual reaction times to a given auditory or visual stimulus were measured. Stimuli were presented while subjects were placed in front of a plate with lightbulbs and plugged-in earphones. The subject had to react as quickly as possible by pushing a button at the appearance of one stimulus (visual or tone) alone (simple tests), or to a specific pattern of sounds or lights (complex tests). In a test on verbal reaction time, the experimenter held a page of words before the subject and told him to read the top line first. Thereafter, the experimenter told him to read all the words on the page as quickly as he could. In the same way, names of colours were presented to the subjects and they were asked to point their finger to a prepared series of squared coloured patches as quickly as possible. Tests were applied 120–150 minutes after drug administration.

As Diagrams 13 and 14 show, virtually no significant difference in the reaction time tests was demonstrated with 50 µg and 100 µg doses compared to placebo. Reaction time to sound alone was significantly impaired with 100 µg. Verbal reaction time tests showed slight but insignificant increases in performance with 50 µg and 100 µg. Significant impairments appeared between placebo and the 50 µg dose in the time taken to read the words. Time to name the colours increased significantly between placebo and 100 µg, and between 50 and 100 µg. In sum, manual reaction time tests were not very sensitive to LSD, but verbal reaction time and colour-naming tests easily detected decreases in performance.

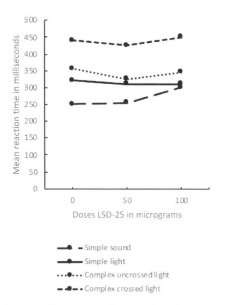

Diagram 13: Mean reaction time, in milliseconds, to each of four tests of manual reaction time to auditory and visual stimuli under two doses of LSD (N=11) (Abramson et al. 1955b)

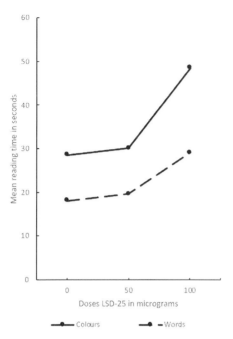

Diagram 14: Mean reaction time, in seconds, to each of two tests of verbal reaction time to visual stimuli under two doses of LSD (N=12) (Abramson et al. 1955b)

Levine et al. (1955b) studied twenty-one healthy volunteers (twelve females and nine males, 22–43 years, mean 29, IQ range 100–137) under different doses of LSD (50, 100, 150, 200 µg). The following tests were used: Bender Gestalt Test, House-Tree-Person Test, Word Association Test, Rorschach Test, Wechsler Bellevue Intelligence Scale, Thematic Apperception Test. In this non-blind study, subjects received a placebo first and on the next occasion the LSD dose. Unfortunately, results for the different dose levels are not presented separately.

In the same experiment, Levine et al. (1955b) tested whether intelligence or intellectual functioning was affected by different doses of LSD. Subjects were tested with the Wechsler-Bellevue Intelligence Scale at two time points (placebo and LSD), weeks or months apart. LSD was given in doses between 50–200 µg (three received 50 µg, sixteen received 100 µg, one received 150 µg, one received 200 µg). Tests were administered 3 to 3.5 hours after drug ingestion.

As the results were only given partially separated by dose, I can make only general statements about them. Subjects who received 50 µg maintained their pre-drug level of intellectual functioning. After 100 µg, virtually all subjects performed much worse, on average more than 10 IQ points below their performance after (inactive) placebo.

Of the subtests, arithmetic, verbal performance and abstract thinking were most affected, while measures for selective recall were quite robust against the influence of LSD. Increased distractibility, inability to concentrate and problems with shifting set obviously interfered with performance. The authors conclude that they have shown a clear-cut overall impairment in the utilization of basic intelligence features, which was dose-dependent.

Eight former morphine addicts took part in the single-blind and placebo-controlled randomized experiment of Isbell et al. (1956) to evaluate responses to varying doses of LSD (0.25, 0.5, 0.75, 1, 1.5, 2 µg/kg). Drugs were given on an empty stomach. Pulse rate, blood pressure, respiratory rate, and rectal temperature were measured at hourly intervals (and, two hours before and eight hours after administration of the LSD). Brief psychiatric examinations were made at two, four, and six hours after ingestion and an MMPI self-rating profile at the 1.5 hour point. The authors reported that doses up to 1 µg/kg induced only mild autonomic changes. Mental effects consisted mainly of anxiety and mood changes, primarily in the "euphoric" direction. However, all non-physical measurements showed significant differences from placebo to all LSD doses except the 0.25 µg/kg dose. Up to 1 µg/kg no significant changes in temperature, pulse rate, or respiratory rate could be demonstrated (Table 4).

Measure	Placebo	0.25 µg/kg	0.5 µg/kg	0.75 µg/kg	1.0 µg/kg
Patellar reflex	0.5	1.18	1.60	1.59	2.10
Pupillary diameter	0.4	1.10	2.29	3.57	3.64
Blood pressure	1.82	2.91	2.93	4.00	4.24
Positive answers to questionnaire	4	26	42	56	30
Clinical grade	0	0.2	0.63	1.5	0.7

Table 4: Effects of increasing doses of LSD on physiological parameters, subjective symptoms and clinical grading by outside observer (Isbell et al. 1956)

In an experiment on tolerance development, subjects of Isbell et al. (1956) received LSD in a single-blind placebo-controlled study. In a substudy, subjects were administered 10, 20, and 30 µg per os at 9:00 am and at 9:00 pm for three days. After this, 75 µg LSD were given to evaluate which effects would still appear.

In a second study, eight males received LSD or placebo per os in randomized order daily at 9:00 am for seven days. The dose was 20 µg, increased every day up to 75 µg on the seventh day. At eight days, 75 µg LSD were given and questionnaires and clinical grading conducted. The authors report that the degree of LSD effects declined rapidly, and "that the differences between the results before and after three days or more of chronic administration were highly significant (p =< 0.01) for all measurements". No subject realized they were dosed with placebo on the later days of the study, which implies that there were no abstinence symptoms and that LSD symptoms disappeared after the build-up of tolerance (Table 5).

Experiment	Questions	Questions	Clinical grade	Clinical grade
	Nontolerant	Tolerant	Nontolerant	Tolerant
1	96 +/-25	22 +/-9	1.95 +/-0.35	0.6 +/-0.2
2	88 +/-31	18 +/-5	1.7 +/-0.5	0.6 +/-0.2

Table 5: Tolerance to LSD after administration for three days (experiment 1) and seven days (experiment 2). Figures are the mean +/- standard errors (Isbell et al. 1956) Nontolerant = after administration of placebo for three days. Tolerant = after administration of LSD for three or seven days.

In a substudy (Isbell et al. 1955), eleven subjects received 10 µg on day one, on day two 20 µg, and on day three 30 µg LSD twice daily. On the fourth day, 75 µg LSD induced only mild mental effects. In all experimental subjects of Isbell et al. (1955, 1956) tolerance was evident in less than seven days. Once tolerance had developed, amounts of LSD four times as great as the doses to which the patients were tolerant were not as effective as the standard dose prior to tolerance. Tolerance was completely lost three days after discontinuation of LSD.

Isbell et al. studied the "possible use of LSD psychosis as a screen for predicting the potential clinical value of new tranquilizing drugs" (Isbell et al 1957: 350) and conducted "blocking experiments" by giving different tranquilizers (chlorpromazine, azacyclonal and reserpine) before or during LSD administration. The double-blind experiments used a cross-over design and randomization with a Latin square design. All subjects were non-psychotic prison inmates incarcerated for narcotic related crimes, with most diagnosed with personality disorders. They were "non-psychotic" and opiate-abstinent (no further information on subjects is given). The fasting subjects received 40 or 60 µg LSD in the morning. Obviously, the number of subjects differed between the different subsets of the experiments from six to nineteen subjects per experiment.

Physiological measures were pupil size, patellar reflex, metabolic rate and resting blood pressure. Mental effects were assessed by the Cold Spring Harbor questionnaire of Jarvik et al. every hour, 2 hours before, and 8 hours after the administration of LSD. A four-point scale was used by an outside observer to grade the intensity of reactions (clinical grading). Two pre-LSD measurements were used as baseline. As shown in Diagram 15, with doses of 40–60 µg LSD produced a significant increase of patellar reflexes and pupil size, a slight increase in blood pressure, a more than 10-fold increase in positive answers (i.e. symptoms were detectable by the subjects) on the questionnaire, and a much higher clinical grading compared to placebo.

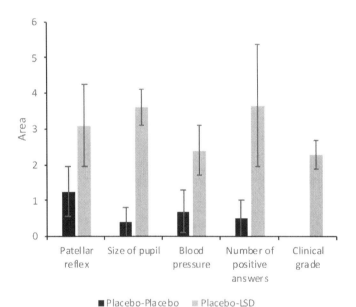

Diagram 15: Some physiological and psychological reactions to 40 µg and 60 µg LSD. The clinical grading was done by an outside observer (Isbell et al. 1957)

With respect to results of the blocking studies, reserpine failed to mitigate the LSD reaction, but reduced pupil size changes caused by LSD. Chlorpromazine (60–75 mg) given 30 minutes before LSD (40 and 60 µg), or during the height of the LSD reaction, reduced positive answers on the questionnaire, clinical grading and pupil size, but did not change blood pressure increases caused by LSD. Frenquel (azacyclonol) in a dose of 20 mg administered two hours before LSD alleviated the reaction to LSD in all measures.

I omit the blocking experiments here and only report the experiments when a low dose of LSD (0.5 µg/kg) was given. The questionnaire developed by Abramson et al. (1955d), behavioural observation (at 15 minute intervals), and introspective reports were used to evaluate effects. The authors reported that LSD at this dose produced mild but characteristic effects. These included "feelings of depersonalization, various paraesthesias, a persistent urge to stretch, feelings of nervousness or general stimulation, and transient visual imagery when the eyes were closed" (p. 654). No quantitative data were presented.

Primac et al. (1957) investigated effects of two different doses of LSD on tests used to detect brain damage. Their subjects were ten normal subjects (six males and four females, age range 18–23 years). A 10 x 10 Latin square design with two placebos was used in this double-blind experiment. Three different drugs were tested (secobarbital, meperidine, and LSD). LSD doses were 50 and 100 µg. Tests were performed 3–3.5 hours after drug ingestion. The Wisconsin Card Sorting Test (WCST) was designed to provide quantitative measures of higher-level cognitive performance. The Continuous Performance Test (CPT) was used to measure sustained attention. It is a visual discrimination task in which the subject must respond within a short period of time to briefly presented stimuli on a visual display. In general, brain-damaged subjects perform more poorly on it than healthy controls (Table 6). The cognitive and associative effort required by the CPT is of a relatively low order. However, no significant changes from either dose of LSD were detected in any of the seven measures used.

Measure	Placebo 1	Placebo 2	50 µg LSD	100 µg LSD
Addition (3 digits), digits per min.	74.1	75.5	64.5	50.4
Addition (9 digits(, digits per min.	42.6	42.1	37.6	25.0
Speed of copying, digits per min.	86.1	84.2	86.7	75.6
Digit symbol, total correct	57.1	58.3	53.0	41.1
Pursuit rotor, see	20.1	21.5	19.2	18.5
Visual discrimination, incorrect	6.5	6.5	9.3	10.8
Tactual perception, no. correct	56.5	52.9	53.3	51.7

Table 6: Neuropsychological performance under two doses of LSD (Primac et al. 1957)

In a similar experiment, Kornetsky and Humphries (1957) and Kornetsky et al. (1957) studied ten normal subjects (six males, four females, 18–23 years old) with a 10 × 10 Latin square design that included two placebos in a double-blind fashion. The other drugs tested were secobarbital and meperidine. LSD was administered in doses of 50 and 100 µg. Tests were additions (three and nine digits), pursuit rotor for hand-eye coordination, digit symbol test, speed of copying numbers, tachistoscopic discrimination, and tactile discrimination. Tests were performed 3–3.5 hours after drug ingestion. In addition, a 46-item symptom questionnaire was applied 30, 60, 90, 150, and 210 minutes after drug ingestion. The score on this questionnaire (total number of symptoms for the four periods) is referred to as the "subjective score". It was reported that LSD at doses of 50 and 100 µg did not significantly affect performance on the pursuit rotor, hand steadiness, or manual reaction time. Verbal reaction time (time to read a series of words), attention and concentration were significantly affected by both doses of LSD.

With respect to intellectual performance and symptom ratings, both LSD doses differed significantly from placebo ($p < 0.05$). The 50 µg dose produced a significant increase in number of symptoms compared to placebo.

Liebert et al. (1958) investigated self- and object-size perception in normal subjects and schizophrenic patients under LSD. I refer here only to the group of normal subjects (n=16), who were dosed with 25 µg (two subjects) and 40 µg (sixteen subjects). The schizophrenic patients received much higher doses. In this single-blind experiment, LSD was given in a randomized order on the first or the second experimental day. The test consisted of subjective size estimations of parts of one's own body (head size and arm's length), size estimation of external objects and size estimation of a drawn figure of the human body. Estimation of head-size and arm-length increased significantly under LSD, while the estimations of the external objects did not change. Size estimation of the drawn human body showed a trend, but was not significant. The results support the hypothesis of the authors that there is an increase in the perceptual size of one's own body, with little or no change in size of external objects. To their eyes the "primitivizing effects of the drug" operate mainly on objects (such as the subject's own body) which are less clearly differentiated from the surroundings and therefore less stabilized by external perception.

Abramson (1959) pooled data from his extensive studies of different doses of LSD and some of its congeners. He used a trained group of five "essentially placebo-negative" subjects for the experiments, to whom LSD and other psychotropic drugs were administered regularly. The experiments were performed under "social test conditions". The drug was administered half an hour before dinner. The remainder of the evening was maintained on a social level with as little intrusion as possible by the researchers into the group's interactions. Here I refer only to the subset of experiments that were related to reactions to LSD.

Subjects received different low doses of 25–50 µg in single-blind experiments, i.e. only the experimenter knows substance and dose. The Cold Spring Harbor questionnaire as developed by Abramson and Jarvik was employed. The number of positive responses to the questionnaire divided by the dose in micrograms of the drug is designated as the Response Index (RI). The higher the value of RI, the greater the response to the drug. The tests were done 1.5–3 hours after drug ingestion.

Table 7 presents data at threshold levels of LSD-25 or slightly above. The author felt that establishing a Group Average RI eliminated many of the variables and gave a more representative measure of psychotropic activity. The authors concluded that "in view of the frequency of false (placebo-positive) reactions either suitable corrections or a screened test group of placebo-negative trained observers must be employed in testing psychotomimetic compounds. If placebo-positive reactions are not encountered in a large series of such tests on man, the method is probably erroneous" (Abramson 1959: 77).

Subject	Dose (µg)	Number of resposnes	Response Index
C.G.	50	34	0.68
	35	25	0.71
	25	34	1.36
	25	19	0.96
	35	22	0.63
P.B.	50	23	0.46
	75	47	0.62
	50	21	0.48
	50	23	0.46
	50	17	0.34
D.V.G.	25	5	0.20
	50	14	0.28

[continued...]

Subject	Dose (µg)	Number of resposnes	Response Index
	35	16	0.46
M.Z.	50	12	0.26
	50	33	0.66
	35	14	0.40
	50	11	0.22
J.G.	50	24	0.50
	25	8	0.32
	25	6	0.24
	25	11	0.44
	50	16	0.32
	35	9	0.29
	50	10	0.20

Table 7: Number of positive responses to symptom questionnaire and calculated Response Index data on different subjects with different doses of LSD (Abramson 1959)

At the beginning of the 1960s there was a vast literature on the subjective effects of LSD, but relatively little systematic testing of performance had been reported for a range of LSD dosages, nor throughout the duration of its action. To determine deficits in complex intellectual performance, the US military conducted studies in their Chemical Warfare Center at Edgewood Arsenal. The studies were conducted on 100 subjects between 1961 and 1966. Results from early tests with doses of 0.5 µg/kg are not available. In 1964, tests were conducted with a dose of 35 µg to examine effects on chess performance. Subjects were trained in lightning chess, which is a very quick form of chess playing with a timer and maximum time limits of 5 or 10 minutes per game. Performance scores were obtained at hourly intervals. Subjects noted only a slight loss of skill at this dose level, which was identical to the objective performance measures (Diagram 16) (Ketchum 2006).

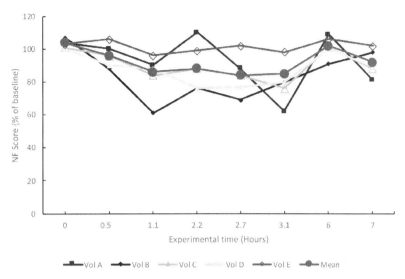

Diagram 16: Effects of 35 µg LSD on chess performance in five subjects (Ketchum 2006)

A recent study on the effects of low-dose LSD

Recently, a randomized, double-blind, placebo-controlled trial was conducted to evaluate subjective and neurocognitive effects of low-dose LSD (Yanakieva et al. 2018). Forty-eight healthy adults (44% female; 56% male) aged between 55 and 75 years took part in the clinical trial, conducted in a hospital. Participants received a medical examination and were found to be healthy. Participants were divided into four groups of twelve. Participants received six single doses of 5 µg (group 1) or 10 µg (group2) or 20 µg (group 3) of LSD or placebo (group 4) every 3 days. Doses were administered prior to a standardized breakfast. Participants were not allowed to drink coffee on dosing days.

Subjective Drug Effects were measured with a Visual Analogue Scale (SDEVAS), ranging from 0 to 100. Results on five items were reported: 1. Do you feel a drug effect?, 2. Do you feel high?, 3. Do your surroundings appear different or changed? 4. Do you feel your ability to concentrate is the same, better, or worse than normal?, and 5. Are you experiencing unusual thoughts? Participants completed the SDEVAS pre-dose and then 30, 60, 90, 120, 150, 180, 240, 300, 360, and 420 min post-dose.

Although there were small numerical differences for some subjective drug effects in the LSD condition, no difference reached statistical significance, i.e. were above chance level. The authors concluded that very low doses of LSD did not produce robust changes in self-report indices of perception, mentation, or concentration. In another part of the experiment, LSD reliably produced over-reproduction of temporal intervals of 2000 ms and longer, most pronounced in the 10 µg dose (less so in the 20 µg condition). Results on effects over the whole treatment interval (18 days) were not reported in the paper (Yanakieva et al. 2018).

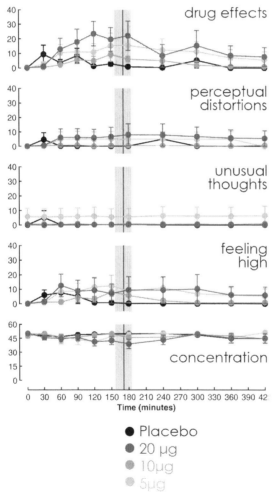

Chart 1: Self-reported subjective drug effects as a function of time

Studies on the detection of low doses

Greiner et al. (1958) tried to investigate the "early stages of toxic psychosis" by establishing the psychophysical response to low doses of LSD. Fourteen healthy male volunteers were given 24 low doses of different amounts (4, 7, 20, 40 μg) of LSD per os. The experiment was claimed to be double-blind, but the number of subjects per group was not given. It appears that three subjects received placebo, two subjects received 4 μg, six subjects 7 μg, two subjects 12 μg, six subjects 20 μg, and five received 40 μg. Subjects were placed in a reclined position in a dark room, and interrupted only for psychological testing for 20 minutes every hour. Questionnaires quantified an estimated deviation from the usual state in respect to perception, body image, alertness, emotion and thought. On another questionnaire, the subject placed themselves along a visual scale between pairs of adjectives describing opposite extremes of mood. Physiological measures such as the galvanic skin response (GSR) and pupil diameter were also taken. According to the authors, physiological changes below a dose of 20 μg were virtually absent, but alterations of the GSR were found with the 7 μg dose without subjects feeling any different to their normal state.

Changes in pupil size were not seen with doses under 12 μg. With 20 μg there were deviations from normal body image, thought and emotion in the period 60–120 minutes post application. On the bipolar dimensions of the second questionnaire, the 20 μg dose resulted in a decrease of alertness, motility, control, thought, and sociability. These remained below the baseline level for the entire experimental day. In the 7 μg group, the bipolar dimensions changed somewhat. Measures of alertness and motility dipped at the third hour, followed by a climb above the baseline level for the rest of the day. Control and thought sank gradually for the first three hours, returning to baseline at the fourth hour. Sociability and hedonic tone increased for the first two hours, dipped sharply at the third hour, but remained above baseline for the entire experimental day. However, it was observed that by the third hour, a sudden tiredness with indifference and low mood appeared. No alterations of thought processes were detected. With the 20 μg dose half of the subjects exhibited euphoria, increased psychomotor tension, and distractibility. By the second hour there was indifference, with physical retardation and social withdrawal, irritability and frequent laughter. Changes in thought such as obsessive thinking, and strange and unreal thoughts were registered. The authors concluded that a threshold dose of 20 μg was confirmed by the experiment, but some effects did appear after lower doses. GSR was the most sensitive physiological measure and it has been linked with neurophysiological arousal. Therefore, the changes seen with the 7 μg dose might be interpreted as evidence for changes in the level of arousal. The shifts in mood with the 20 μg dose were not consciously perceived by the subjects, but the authors felt that a lability and shifting in mood was the main consequence of low doses of LSD.

De Maar et al. (1960) studied mental and physical effects of the neuroleptic drug reserpine, and the antidepressant drug iproniazid, on the LSD reaction. The authors saw the problem was that most conventional psychometric tests do not appropriately measure LSD-induced alterations, especially when it comes to distinguishing between different dose levels (with 25 μg intervals). In contrast, the subjects themselves—having received LSD several times— became able to quantify the dose given with a high degree of precision. Subjects were sixteen male prison inmates (mean age of 34, IQ 90–123), with some psychopathic deviant MMPI profiles. The double-blind tests were done in eight groups of two each. Blood pressure, pulse rate, pupil diameter, oral temperature, and hand steadiness were measured hourly. Oral doses of 25, 50, and 100 μg LSD were administered. Each subject had experienced during his training the effects of doses of 25, 50, and 100 μg LSD, at least four times. Mental effects were assayed in an interview 3 hours after drug ingestion and a retrospective written report by the subjects.

Here only the LSD experiments are reported, not the drug combinations. In 15 LSD-alone experiments, subjects always identified correctly whether they received LSD, independent of dose (Table 8).

LSD dose	Correct estimate of dose
25 μg	26.3 +/- 3.8
50 μg	57.9 +/- 3.9
100 μg	91.1 +/- 8.5

Table 8: Mean of doses reported and standard error of the mean. Quantitative evaluation of LSD medication received (de Maar et al. 1960)

In 122 administrations of LSD, the subjects reported an LSD-like effect in 113 instances. "'No LSD" was reported 49 times. Statistical analysis showed that the ability of the subjects to discriminate between the different doses was highly significant. However, if a dose of 25 μg was used, the number of detections dropped to ca. 25%.

The log-dose response relationship is significantly linear (p>0.01 and <0.05). The curve is straight from 25–100 μg. There is a curvature from zero to 25 *μg*. It shows that this group of subjects made highly reliable estimates about the doses, based on the intensity of their symptoms.

Abramson and Rolo (1967) tested subjective reactions to low doses of LSD and psilocybin, to see whether subjects could detect lower doses. To assay effects of the drugs the Cold Spring Harbor questionnaire as designed by the Abramson group to measure symptoms produced by LSD was employed. Substances were given by mouth half an hour before the evening meal. Experiments were conducted on "a group of 6 essentially placebo negative subjects", i.e. subjects who did not react significantly to placebo in previous experiments. Their age range was 33–45 years and their weight range was 68–82 kg. The experiments were run blind or double-blind in groups of six subjects. The same six subjects were repeatedly dosed with either LSD, psilocybin, congeners of LSD, or placebo. Some subjects in the group received placebo while others received the drugs. Subjects were informed that they would receive LSD, psilocybin, a placebo, or a congener of LSD. The authors report on 150 experiments. Results of the few tolerance experiments in this series are not given here.

LSD Dose	Number of trials	Correct estimate	False estimate	Lower estimate	Higher estimate
20 μg	1		1		
25 μg	8	7	1		
35 μg	18	18			
50 μg	19	10		9	
Placebo	22	8	4		

Table 9: Number of trials and guesses/estimates by six "placebo-negative" subjects (Abramson & Rolo 1967)

Results show mostly correct guesses, but also 20% responses to placebo (Table 9). This appears to be a high response rate, considering these are selected and trained "placebo-negative" subjects. One should note a possible influence from the partially non-blind experimenters. However, these experiments seem to prove that subjects experienced with low doses are usually able to detect a dose of 25 µg and dose differences in the range of 25–50 µg LSD.

Studies on interpersonal effects

Lennard et al. (1956) were the first to report on the effects of low doses of LSD on interpersonal communication. In their experiment, groups of four people were given LSD or placebo and their interactions observed. It was the aim of the study to "specify the dimensions along which interpersonal communication is modified" (Lennard et al. 1956: 185).

Four healthy volunteers (three females, one male, age range 22–26 years, average weight 135 pounds) with an intelligence which was described as "superior to very superior" as measured by IQ testing, were given LSD or placebo in several different arrangements. One was that two participants received 50 µg and the other two 100 µg. In other experiments, two subjects got LSD, the other two got placebo. A few months later the same group was given just plain water as a placebo, but with the question left open as to whether they had received LSD. Some of the subjects had received LSD before the experiment (it is not stated how long before). All group sessions were recorded on tape. The authors had some hypotheses to be tested by their experiment, but as these are not relevant to our interests, we do not give extensive details here about them, nor their research design. In short, they were interested in the following propositions:

- Quantity of continuous speech for the group and the individual will be less under LSD;
- Density of speech is expected to be less under LSD;
- Number of unfinished statements will be greater under LSD;
- Number of interruptions will be greater under LSD.

The most important of the many variables used were: quantity of speech, direction of speech (who initiates; amount of communication; to whom addressed); other characteristics of communication (interruptions, unfinished thought units etc.).

Hypothesis 1 was confirmed, but no relationship between LSD dose and decrease of these parameters emerges from the data. One explanation may be the individual tolerance or sensitivity rather than the absolute dosage. The authors observed that the composition of the group makes a difference in respect to the individuals in this proactive rate. In each case the highest value appears when an individual interacts in groups where he is under the condition "normal" while some or most of the others are under varying doses of LSD. To explain this finding, one should bear in mind that the communications system of a group represents an equilibrium so that, if one unit of the system fails to do its part, other units of the system will then make up for it, i.e. the presence of individuals (on LSD) whose proactions are decreased operates to increase the proactions of those who are not under the influence of LSD. Hypothesis 2 was not confirmed by the data. Density of speech was virtually unaltered. Hypothesis 3 was confirmed as there is a tendency for communication to "trail off" under LSD and it was not concluded meaningfully in a lot of cases. Hypothesis 4 was not confirmed, but the opposite was true. The relationship between interruptions and unfinished statements is complementary, but in an inverse fashion. One may speculate that individuals will be most likely to interrupt someone else when they are clearly conscious of, and have succinctly formulated, the ideas that they wish to communicate.

In summary, verbal output on the part of the group members under the influence of the drug was restricted or shortened. In groups in which some members received LSD and others did not, there was a tendency for non-drugged subjects to increase their communication output. It appears that drug-free individuals made up for the "deficiency" in verbal communication of those on LSD. When all group members were given LSD, a marked reduction of negative interpersonal responses was observed. Psychological experiments have shown that disruptive interpersonal behaviour is reduced when group members operate under a common threat (in this case the "LSD intoxication"). Interestingly, the ratio between amounts of task activity and socio-emotional activity does not differ between the "normal" and the LSD group. The ratios of questions to answers, and of orientation and evaluation responses, was higher in the LSD groups. Compared to changes in individual functioning, patterns of group communication were much less impaired.

Hausner and Dolezal (1966) conducted a therapy study in which the patients were treated with LSD. It was intented to compare results from individual and group therapeutic settings. The patients received 50 or 100 µg LSD. Under the group condition, 5–10 patients on LSD were mixed with those on placebo. The conditions treated were neurotic and personality disorders. No details about the reactions of the patients on the 50 µg dose were given, but the result of the investigation was that LSD given in individual sessions gave better results for the patients.

Vojtechovsky et al. (1972) conducted twenty-two double-blind experiments (20 µg LSD) in twelve healthy students. None of them had previous experience with LSD. Subjects were paired and dosed. They received either LSD-placebo, LSD-LSD or placebo-placebo. Social performance was observed in the laboratory and while performing social contacts in town (e.g. shopping, making travel arrangements, etc.). The most frequent symptoms induced by LSD were euphoria and unmotivated smiling. All symptoms could be significantly better controlled while in town than in the laboratory. No unusual behaviour emerged under the stress of social tasks.

Effects on glucose metabolism

Mayer-Gross et al. (1951, 1952) investigated glucose metabolism with low doses of LSD. Twenty-four healthy volunteers received 40 µg LSD whilst fasting, in a double-blind study. One and two hours after administration, blood samples were taken. All laboratory parameters measured were identical with placebo and LSD, except glucose and hexose monophosphate.

Glycogen is the major carbohydrate reserve of the body. Hexose monophosphate (HMP) is the first stage in the process of mobilizing this reserve. Without movement or stress (as in these experiments) it is expected that glycogen would not be used, and therefore no increase of HMP blood levels would be expected, as seen in the controls.

Under LSD, plasma levels of glucose increased about 9 mg/100 ml after the first hour, and 11 mg/100 ml after the second hour. With LSD, HMP increased on average 1.7 mg/100 ml after the first hour and showed a decrease of 0.3 mg/100 ml after two hours, whereas the range in the control group was stable at 2.3–2.4 mg/100 ml. The increase of HMP in the LSD-treated subjects points to a higher carbohydrate metabolism, which is also indicated by the slightly, but insignificantly elevated glucose levels (Tables 10 and 11).

Subject	Empty stomach Experiment	Empty stomach Control	1 hr. Experiment	1 hr. Control	2 hrs. Experiment	2 hrs. Control
1	81	77	87	81	87	83
2	64	78	81	81	81	88
3	81	81	81	83	81	83
4	81		77		77	
5	93	93	91	81	104	81
6	93	96	104	104	116	82
7	81	81	70	81	81	81
8	81	92	104	87	81	81
9	69	90	127	81	104	81
10	81	81	81	93	104	85
Mean	82	81	91	80	93	83
Mean increase/ decrease			-9	1	-11	-2

Table 10: Alterations of glucose blood levels after administration of LSD (40–70 μg, dependent on body weight) (Mayer-Gross et al. 1952)

Subject	Empty stomach Experiment	Empty stomach Control	1 hr. Experiment	1 hr. Control	2 hrs. Experiment	2 hrs. Control
1	18.1	14.7	22.6	12.2	16.7	12.1
2	8.7	8.3	17.3	6.7	8.4	6.2
3	15.7	14.2	22.3	12.1	17.8	11.3
4	12.1		18.7		13.2	
5	16.3	16.7	18.7	10.2	10.1	9.4
6	7.6	8.2	10.3	7.1	4.2	6.9
7	11.5	14.9	13.7	12.5	12.0	8.2
8	9.4	8.6	9.7	6.2	6.2	6.1
9	10.1	9.8	10.2	7.2	6.7	7.9
10	8.7	9.2	8.6	7.6	4.7	7.3
Mean	12.2	11.1	13.9	8.8	11.9	8.7
Mean increase			1.7	2.3	0.3	2.4

Table 11: Alterations of hexosemonophosphate blood levels after administration of LSD (40–70 μg, dependent on body weight) (Mayer-Gross et al. 1952)

Effects on adrenaline levels

Liddel and Weil-Malherbe (1953) gave 40–60 μg LSD in an unblinded study to three mentally ill patients (diagnoses not given) to examine blood adrenaline levels. Blood samples were taken 30, 60, 90, 120, 150, 180, and 210 minutes after ingestion. The blood level of adrenaline changed markedly (Diagram 17). With intravenous administration, the same doses of LSD led to the same changes but these began earlier and were quicker to return to normal. Blood sugar did not change significantly. With respect to clinical observation, the authors found that after an initial phase of relaxation the drug produced an aggravation of the clinical picture and abreaction occurred frequently.

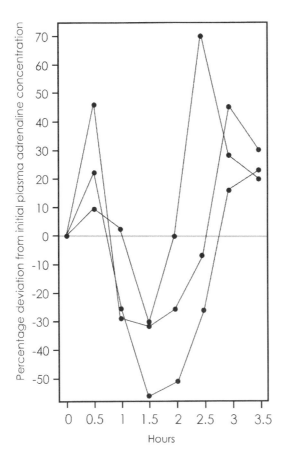

Diagram 17: The effect of 40–60 μg LSD per os on the adrenaline concentrations in blood plasma (Liddell & Weil-Malherbe 1953).

Effects on sleep and dreaming

The first experiments on the influence of LSD (open, n = 3, 25 µg) on sleep in humans showed signs of increased restlessness and extended REM phases (Toyoda, 1964). Muzio et al. (1966) investigated effects of LSD on sleep, especially REM sleep (REMS). Due to LSD´s imagery-evoking properties, the researchers hypothesized that an enhancement of REMS by LSD might elucidate hallucinatory mechanisms. In this experiment, twelve subjects reported on their typical sleep pattern for three nights prior to the experiment. One group received placebo, the other LSD, prior to consecutive night recordings. In order to avoid excessive arousals and awakenings, very small doses of LSD were used. Thirty-six LSD doses of 6 to 40 µg were administered. In eleven of the twelve subjects, LSD induced a 20–245% prolongation of either the first or second REM period. These effects occurred with doses of 0.14 and 0.73 µg/kg. In nine cases in which the drug doses were 0.08 to 0.55 µg/kg, LSD did not alter the sleep EEG cycle but caused moderate increases of body motility. In some cases, arousals continually interrupted sleep. Successive experimental series were usually correlated with greater prolongations of REMS periods, but the relationship was not uniform. Although there were inconsistent responses to the midrange of LSD doses (0.33–0.55 µg/kg) there was a trend towards longer first REMS periods following higher doses. Subsequent REMS periods for the most part were abbreviated, but continued to recur in the normal pattern at 70–90 minute intervals. There was no consistent increase in total REMS. During the night following the LSD, night recordings were comparable to control nights.

Torda et al. (1968) gave intravenous infusions of LSD to explore changes during sleep. Two healthy subjects slept for ten nights in the sleep laboratory. Seven nights were placebo nights, and on the other three nights subjects received an intravenous infusion of 50 *µg* LSD over ten minutes while they were asleep. LSD reduced the latency to the next REMS period (10–19 minutes instead of the usual 40–60 min) and the incidence of REMS.

Studies of sleep deprivation on LSD's effects

In a substudy of a larger LSD trial, Bliss and Clark (1959) gave four healthy volunteers 0.5 and 1.0 µg/kg LSD per os. Psychological tests and behavioural observations were made. In one part of the experiment, subjects were awake for 48 hours before LSD was administered. A dose of 0.5 µg/kg without sleep deprivation led to "no hallucinations", but after sleep deprivation the same dose led to more "hallucinations" than 1 µg/kg LSD in non-sleep deprived subjects. According to the authors, this result implies that "... sleep deprivation enhances the disruptive effects of LSD-25 upon ego functions" (p. 357). It was also known to some psycholytic therapists that when patients had bad, or no, sleep in advance of their psycholytic therapy sessions, the reaction to the drug would be more intense (Leuner 1994).

Low-dose LSD as an active placebo

McGothlin et al. (1967) designed a study to investigate "long-lasting effects of LSD on normal [subject]s" using measures of personal values and orientation and other psychological tests. The subjects of their double-blind placebo-controlled study were paid male graduate students. There were three groups: group 1 (200 µg LSD), group 2 (25 µg LSD), and group 3 (25 mg amphetamine). There was no mixing of treatment groups within sessions and each subject received the same dosage at each of his three sessions. The drug was given at 8:00 am. The sessions were held in a tastefully decorated room and subjects were asked to lie on the couch, and listen to music through earphones, whilst wearing sleep shades.

The main reason for using two control groups was the anticipation that the 25 µg LSD group would experience sufficient auditory and visual changes to believe they had received LSD, and thus provide a more adequate control for prior expectations. In contrast to this, only 25% of the 25 µg group subjects thought that they had received LSD on one or more of their sessions. With respect to results, there were no significant differences between the amphetamine and 25 µg LSD group, and they were combined into a single control group. Therefore, very few data on the 25 µg control group were presented separately. There were much lower acute subjective effects in the 25 µg LSD group than in the amphetamine group. As expected, virtually no changes were registered with respect to long-term changes in the 25 µg group, while the 200 µg LSD group showed significant pre-/post-drug differences.

During the 1960s, some research projects used high-dose LSD sessions and a specific setting to treat alcoholics. Within this "psychedelic" treatment paradigm, patents received 250–500 µg LSD per os to induce experiences of self-insight and mystical experiences in order to achieve personality transformation (Hoffer & Osmond 1968). To prove efficacy of a medical treatment, the placebo-controlled, double-blind experiment is the gold standard. It serves to minimize effects of suggestion and expectancy. If a substance has strong and obvious effects, such as those provoked by LSD, it makes sense to use an active placebo, which induces some of LSD's effects, but which is assumed to not have the same efficacy in treating the target condition. One option to use as an active placebo is to give a very low dose of the same drug, to induce some effects to "fool" subject and experimenter. In this way it is hoped to preserve blindness of subject and experimenter regarding the drug/placebo condition.

In one of the last controlled studies to treat alcoholics with LSD therapy, Kurland et al. (1971) used 450 µg LSD in one group and 50 µg as an active placebo in the control group. Clinical studies have consistently shown a linear dose-response relationship with LSD administration in symptom scores (cf. Klee et al. 1961). Therefore, it was expected that the low-dose group would experience only a few mild LSD effects, which would help to preserve blindness in regard to whether a full dose had been given. All patients were treated alike during the preparation and the LSD sessions. Main outcome measures were personality tests and drinking behaviour. However, the researchers were astonished that the high-dose group showed no significantly greater improvement over the low-dose group on any test variable (Diagrams 18 and 19). With respect to abstinence from alcohol, the high-dose group showed a significantly better result at the six-month time point, but not at the 12- and 18-month follow ups. "The fact that the low-dose group did as well as it did probably reflects the intense preparation therapy and LSD session which they received. Many of our 50 µg sessions involved considerable abreaction and catharsis of psychodynamically charged material" (Kurland et al. 1971: 92). The authors recommended against using low-dose LSD as an active placebo in future studies.

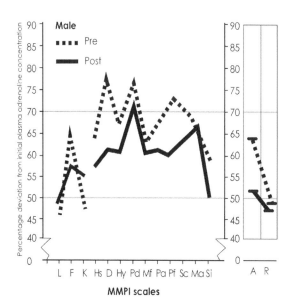

Diagram 18: Composite pre- and post-treatment Minnesota Multiphasic Personality Inventory (MMPI) profiles of 38 low- dose patients (Kurland et al. 1971).

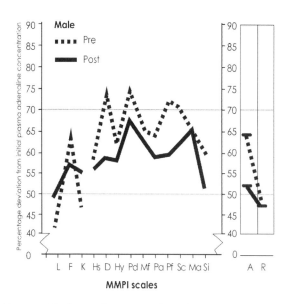

Diagram 19: Composite pre- and post-treatment Minnesota Multiphasic Personality Inventory (MMPI) profiles of 81 high dose patients (Kurland et al. 1971).

Low-dose LSD in psychotherapy

As a result of the first clinical studies with LSD by Stoll (1947) and Condrau (1947), it was suggested that the intensification of psychological and cathartic reactions by LSD might be advantageously used in psychotherapy.

A few years later, Busch and Johnson (1953) used doses of 20–40 µg LSD on 29 patients with psychoneurotic disorders in a non-blind experiment. Usually women were dosed with 30 µg and men with 40 µg. Maximum effects were registered 120–150 minutes after ingestion, with four hours being the usual duration of action. The somatic effects exhibited by most of the patients, in order of their frequency were: gastric distress, nausea, tremor, dizziness, dilation of pupils, and increase in pulse rate. The patients exhibited increases in movement, responses to stimulation, talkativeness, and emotional expression. The authors concluded that "LSD-25 may offer a means for more daily gain access to the chronically withdrawn patients. It may also serve as a new tool for shortening psychotherapy" (Busch and Johnson 1950: 243). These findings led the pharmaceutical company Sandoz in Switzerland, where LSD had been discovered, to give the following advice in the prospectus about their new product. With respect to its use in psychotherapy "… to elicit release of repressed material and provide mental relaxation, particularly in anxiety states and obsessional neuroses. The initial dose is 25 µg. This dose is increased at each treatment by 25 µg until the optimum dose (usually between 50 and 200 µg) is found" (Sandoz 1951).

The publication of Busch and Johnson's article gave rise to the paradigm of "psycholytic therapy". This approach uses low doses of LSD or psilocybin to induce a regressive state in which emotions, thoughts and accompanying associations, increased mental imagery and catharsis were aimed at, to intensify and shorten psychodynamic psychotherapy. At the time, a series of 10–30 low-dose sessions were conducted within a course of conventional psychoanalytic psychotherapy. The doses varied between 25–150 µg, with 50–100 µg being the most used (cf. Leuner 1981, Sandison 1954, Buckman 1967, Geert-Jörgensen 1961). Hanscarl Leuner was one of the major proponents of psycholytic therapy in Europe. When he started his research and therapeutic work, he used doses of 30 µg in day-long sessions and repeated these sessions every week over a period 12 to 20 weeks (Leuner 1958, 1959). Similar results were reported by Roubicek (1962). Abramson (1956) used a related technique with doses of 50 µg (in one case 20 µg) to treat neurotic patients. Because his patients showed some significant perceptual and psychological changes, Abramson recommended keeping the patient in the office for at least five hours after ingestion of the drug.

German psychiatrist Walter Frederking used 30–60 µg LSD in 10–20 serial psycholytic sessions. He found this procedure very useful. According to Frederking, the administration of LSD,

> *led to states of a dream-like nature with experiences that were clearly remembered afterwards. The procedure is indicated when it is desirable to shorten a course of therapy, reactivate a stalled treatment of a neurosis, and for the purpose of breaking down affect or memory blocks. A psychocathartic effect is almost uniformly produced.*
>
> (Frederking 1955: 265)

Abramson (1955) used 20–40 µg LSD for therapeutic interviews. In this paper, a verbatim transcript of a four-hour interview under 40 µg is reported. At the height of the LSD reaction, which was observed between 1.5–3 hours, the patient "was able to integrate many facts, and simultaneously bring up data she previously was unable to discuss without overwhelming anxiety" and she utilized the LSD state "to reduce the defensive mechanisms and to reconstruct what was learned thereby to her psychic benefit". According to the observations of the author;

> *ego-depression does occur in the normal individual taking up to 50 micrograms by mouth, I believe that one other process goes on simultaneously, and that process is ego-enhancement, or reinforcement. The ability of the individual under small doses of LSD-25 to face preconscious or unconscious material and to integrate this material into the dynamic forces of the ego-structure is not part of a loss of ego, but rather that of a reinforced ego which functions more effectively under the drug, in the presence of the therapist.*
>
> (Abramson 1955: 153)

In a double-blind experiment by Gordon (1975), psychotherapy patients were dosed either with LSD (50–100 µg), or amphetamine as an active placebo, or with an inactive placebo. Subjects were told that they would receive different doses of LSD in all experiments.

Most of the authors using LSD in psychotherapy suggested a stronger expression of affects from this practice, but this was not confirmed by this study. No separate results were given for the different dose levels. As mentioned, most psycholytic therapists used LSD doses above 50 µg, generally in the range of 60–100 µg. However, it was usual practice in the late 1950s and 1960s to titrate the dose during the first few sessions until the optimal dose level for each patient was determined. Therefore many psycholytic therapists used a dose of LSD as low as 25 or 50 µg for the first sessions, adding 25 µg in each of the following sessions until an optimum dose was reached, usually in the 50–150 µg range (cf. Eisner and Cohen 1958, Ling and Buckman 1963, Gnirss 1965, Soskin 1973).

7.2 Effects of low-dose LSD on pathological conditions

Effects on patients with schizophrenia

Hoch and Cattell (1952) studied reactions of humans to LSD and related drugs, partially in the context of the US Army's search for "truth drugs" (cf. Passie & Benzenhöfer 2018). Their aim was to study "the personality structure of different individuals under drug stress" and to use these drugs for "diagnostic, prognostic, and therapeutic purposes" (Hoch & Cattell 1952: 583). Tests referred to in this publication were conducted with schizophrenic patients (24 males and 35 females) with doses in the range of 10–120 µg. No differential data on dosages were reported, just clinical impressions, and these were from a lot of experiments, e.g. "below 60 µg, and sometimes even over 60 µg, we found the symptoms produced to be unreliable" (Hoch & Cattell 1952: 581).

It is a well-known side effect of cortisone, an endogenous hormone, that as a medication it can induce "mental disturbances" in mentally normal patients. LSD can also produce abnormal mental states. Researchers were therefore interested to know whether premedication with cortisone would have an influence on the sensitivity of schizophrenic patients to LSD. Five young schizophrenics with normal physical conditions, who were stable (quasi-healthy) for some months with respect to their psychoses were treated. During a 40-day period, subjects were given oral doses of LSD at intervals of 3–4 days. The starting dose was 10 µg. The dosage was increased by 5–10 µg at each successive trial day. The subjects were interviewed by two psychiatrists at a constant time after ingestion. Subjects were not aware of the nature of the drug. The dosage was increased until the visual disturbances characteristic for LSD intoxication were induced. This dosage in a given subject was arbitrarily designated as his "LSD threshold". The subjects were then started on cortisone at a dose of 50 mg per day. After six days of cortisone, the threshold dose was repeated and the effects observed. A threshold dose of LSD could be determined in four of the five subjects. This was 70 µg in two subjects, and 60 and 80 µg in the others. The fifth subject, however, over the course of 15 trials in doses from 10–130 µg never admitted any effects from LSD other than feeling "drowsy". Sub-threshold doses of LSD in subjects 1–4 produced a variety of minor effects. They were generally more alert and mildly euphoric but physically underactive. There was some smiling and giggling. They described themselves variously as feeling "drunk", numb", "dizzy", "confused", or on "Cloud 8". According to the authors, some psychological effects were evident even with the smallest doses. None of the subjects showed serious behavioural disturbances. The effects subsided within 4–6 hours. No significant changes in sensitivity to LSD were observed in any of the subjects with cortisone premedication (Clark & Clark 1956).

Effects on patients with depression

In an observational study, Savage (1952) studied effects of LSD on psychiatric patients to determine whether LSD would produce a euphoric state of therapeutic value in interviews, or a betterment of clinical state. He treated 20 subjects (five normal subjects and 15 severely depressed patients of all diagnostic categories). They were given a course of LSD for four weeks. Depressives started with 20 µg, which was increased daily to a point where a definite psychophysical effect could be observed. This point varied in different patients from 20 µg to 60 µg for most people, but in a few cases 100 µg. Measurements were carried out before, during and after the course of treatment. Follow-up studies continued for about six months.

It was found that a dose of 20 µg produced depersonalisation/derealisation (and some imagery enhancement) in most healthy controls, but the Wechsler-Bellevue Test on memory and comprehension showed no difference. With respect to the betterment of depressives, the cases were different, as illustrated by the following case vignettes.

Case 1:
Initial dose 20 µg up to 60 µg four weeks. Mild euphoria was frequent and sustained after the obvious physiological reaction had worn off. He improved for about a fortnight. Then he began to suffer occasional distressing symptoms, ... shortness of breath, headache, tinnitus ... feeling 'jittery and nervous'... associated with marked feelings of hostility. His sensorium remained clear. After one week he was feeling better than he had in months [and was] discharged as recovered.

Case 2:

LSD for a month. No therapeutic effect ... with doses as high as 100 μg.

Case 3:

On admission depressive and suicidal. 20–70 μg for a month. Occasionally complained of distorted vision. ... he was able to express some feelings of anger. ... After 3 weeks he became less defensive ... repressed affect was elicited, but his basic personality remained unchanged." The author concluded from these experiments: *"About half of the patients developed lessening of depression, ... but unless this improvement was followed up by psychotherapy patients had difficulty in maintaining improvement"* and *"... LSD does not appear to have a significant therapeutic advantage in depressed states, although it appears of value as an adjuvant in a certain number of cases.*
(Savage 1952: 899/900)

An experiment by Sloane and Doust (1954) with 14 normal volunteers and nineteen mentally ill patients (psychiatric inpatients, twelve depressives, endogenous and neurotic subtypes, age range 20–40 years, average age 28). All subjects received 40 μg LSD per os and were evaluated with tests for attention and concentration, time estimation, eidetic imagery, speed of oscillation (Necker Cube), the Wechsler Memory Scale, and for motor efficiency. Physiological measures included cardiovascular response to stress, oximetry, and the Cold Pressor Stress Test (CPT). In respect to time estimation it was found that the LSD subjects perceived a shorter apparent duration (Placebo 13.4, LSD 11.2). The Cold Pressor Test (CPT) is a cardiovascular test performed by immersing the hand into a container of ice water for one minute and measuring changes in blood pressure and heart rate due to systemic sympathetic activation by release of adrenaline. This physiological stress response produces a marked fall in a person's reaction time. Under LSD the extent of this fall was significantly increased ($p = 0.01$) and the duration of the fall was prolonged ($p = 0.02$).

None of the other objective measures showed any significant difference from placebo, including blood pressure and oxygen consumption. In respect to subjective experience, "perceptual changes were certainly not notable and the illusions manifested were minimal in degree" (Sloane & Doust 1954: 141). For an outside observer, the clinical changes with 40 µg were "not gross, although euphoria, when present was unmistakable. ... In general, it appeared that slight, although clinically apparent, changes produced by the drug were difficult to verify objectively" (Sloane & Doust 1954: 141). Results were not presented separately for the different types of patients. In one depressive patient, mood slightly lightened with 40 µg, but he became suicidal on 80 µg. The authors found that, "in general mood changes seemed dependent upon the original affective state of the subject, equanimity and cheerfulness tending toward euphoria, whereas anxiety and depression were usually heightened". Even if some neurotic depressive patients showed some improvement, the authors concluded that "... the drug would seem of little therapeutic value in depressive states" (Sloane & Doust 1954: 141).

Effects on patients with obsessive-compulsive disorder (OCD)

It has been repeatedly reported that psychedelics can have a symptom-reducing influence on symptoms of OCD (Moreno et al. 2006).

A report by Reda and Rambelli (1961) deals with the treatment of nineteen patients with OCD with two to five doses of 25–50 µg LSD (p.o. or injected intramuscularly). No additional psychotherapy was provided. A few times, the administration of placebo instead of LSD was used in the course of the treatments. The authors reported a non-specific "mental irritation", sometimes associated with anxiety, sometimes with serenity. A few patients reported themselves free of obsessional ideas, but only for short periods during the acute intoxication. However, no clinically relevant improvement was seen in any patient.

Effects on patients with epilepsy

Schwarz et al. (1956) argued that Hughlings Jackson's classic description of the paroxysmal dream state in patients with temporal lobe epilepsy (TLE) has features reminiscent of effects of LSD-25 and mescaline; hallucinations, perceptual illusions, affect disturbances, forced thinking, and automatisms in conjunction with a relatively clear sensorium. Patients with this condition can sometimes even travel to another city (which they are familiar with) and make their way to a specific place, without being "conscious". There are similarities to sleepwalking, where "competent" handling of environmental circumstances is not unusual. The authors attempted to trigger seizures by means of these two drugs. Three patients with TLE received 50 μg of LSD. The experiment showed that "LSD and mescaline did not provoke psychic auras [or seizures]. EEG changes were minimal and were associated with the action of mescaline and LSD, rather than as an activation of a focus" (Schwarz et al. 1956: 280).

Effects on patients with migraine

Sicuteri (1963) tested LSD and different LSD derivatives for the prophylactic treatment of migraine headaches. It had been shown at the time that migraine sufferers excrete more serotonin metabolites during their attacks. Some essential data were missing in Sicuteri's publication, but the prophylactic efficacy of LSD (50–100 μg) was estimated to be in the medium range. This did not lead to the use of LSD for this purpose, because derivatives of LSD (e.g. UML-491, lysergic acid-1-methyl-butanolamide or methysergide) were found to be more effective. However, in a later publication, Sicuteri (1977: 57) reported that "LSD is a good migraine prophylactic agent in non-hallucinogenic doses, such as 0.1–0.2 mg/kg [i.e. 7 15 μg] ... ." This suggests Sicuteri had experience with the use of very small doses of LSD for prophylactic purposes.

Ling and Buckman (1963) have treated (in a series of psychosomatic cases) nine patients with migraines. All patients received between two to nine sessions with low doses such as 50 μg (not all doses are given), sometimes combined with a low dose of methylphenidate (usually 20 mg). The authors considered migraine a partially psychosomatic disease. The patients had a typical kind of course of psycholytic low-dose therapy, with experience of childhood memories, intensification of emotions, abreactions and significant self-insights. The authors report that five patients were healed from their migraines completely (follow up at 12 to 18 months), two had "partial success" and two were unchanged. The authors interpret their success as related to the patients' neurotic tensions being improved by the treatment. Today it is established that substances like LSD and psilocybin can be helpful with cluster headaches and migraines, primarily through a neurobiological mechanism (cf. Schindler et al. 2015).

Fanciullacci et al. (1974) investigated the hypothesis as to whether migraine sufferers were more sensitive to drugs interacting with the serotonin system. Two groups received LSD. Group 1 consisted of thirty normal subjects (18 females, 12 males, age 25–60 years, average 43.3). Group 2 consisted of 36 migraine sufferers (24 females, 12 males, age 22–62 years, average 43.8). All subjects were dosed every three days at 9:00 am in a double-blind randomized scheme with 0.35 µg/kg (= 20–25 µg). Subjects were "questioned about their sensations" at 4, 8, and 12 hours after drug ingestion. Three categories were used to describe the subject's reactions (1 = no reaction; 2 = simple psycho-affective reactions; 3 = psycho-affective reaction plus perceptual alterations). In response to the given dose 73% of the normal subjects reported "no reaction" and 27% reported a response of category 2 (Diagram 20). No normal subject reported a reaction of category 3. In contrast, 25% of the migraine sufferers had no reaction, 57% reported a category 2 response and 18% a category 3 response. The statistical evaluation (Mann-Whitney U Test) showed a highly significant difference ($p =< 0.001$) between normal subjects and headache sufferers. The authors concluded that the sensitivity of migraine sufferers to LSD was much higher compared to normal subjects, which they conjectured might depend on a different permeability at the blood brain barrier and/or a supersensitivity at the receptor level.

It is noteworthy that only a quarter of the normal subjects had any response to 20–25 µg LSD. However, in this experiment, the experimenters were not blind to the drug/placebo condition and the headache sufferers might have been more prone to be sensitive to "pathological effects" because of their painful disease.

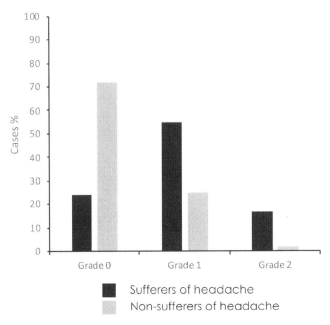

Diagram 20: Migraine-headache sufferers exhibit increased psychological sensitivity to LSD, in comparison to non-headache sufferers (p < 0.001) (Fanciullacci et al. 1974).

Fadiman (2018) has reported that most people who wrote about microdosing with migraines report up to a 90% reduction in frequency. According to Fadiman, one subject has reported the she has been microdosing for three years which is working just fine.

Use of low doses of LSD for the treatment of cluster headache

In 1996, a Scotsman found that the ingestion of LSD helped with his cluster headache. After further experimentation he established a relationship existed between taking LSD and the disappearance of his headaches. He posted his "discovery" on the internet and shortly thereafter many cluster headache sufferers tried to treat themselves with doses of LSD and psilocybin (usually in the medium dose range). Sewell et al. (2006) conducted a survey of these patients and found that these psychedelics were reportedly quite effective in aborting the acute attacks as well as having a "preventative effect" on cluster headache periods. These periods typically go on in "clusters", for example for two periods a year a patient has daily headaches for a month or more, but between these, they have longer, headache-free intervals. The use of LSD or psilocybin appears to lengthen these headache-free periods quite a bit. According to some authors, a scheme of taking three doses with five days in between (i.e. day 1, day 5, and day 10) gives the strongest preventative effect (Sewell et al. 2006, Karst et al. 2010).

There are also reports from cluster headache sufferers who have used microdosing to cope with their illness. In a recent internet survey on cluster headache patients, websites and forums, Andersson et al. (2017) found microdosing frequently discussed and recommended. According to the patients, microdosing is preferred, because it does not interfere with daily routines, avoids significant psychoactive effects, enables more frequent dosing, and might prevent adverse effects. Microdosing appeared to be used primarily for prophylactic effects. However, there is no scientific research or evidence supporting this course of action, and some patients reported inadequate therapeutic effects from small doses. A technique of using "frequent microdosing" is also mentioned, but no numbers or specific patterns of administrations are presented. The substances used for "microdose treatment" were mostly psilocybin, LSD, and some synthetic psychedelic tryptamines. A few patients reported adverse effects such as increased perspiration and problems with focus and unexpected emotional experiences from microdosing for the treatment of cluster headaches with LSD or psilocybin.

Fadiman (2018) has reported to the author of the present book that most people with cluster headaches need higher doses for a successful treatment, although for a few people, some of whom have reported to Fadiman, microdoses have been enough.

Effects on patients with phantom limb pain

Presumably following the observation of Kuromaru et al. (1967), Fanciullacci et al. (1977) treated five males and two females (aged 25–78 years) with "sub-hallucinogenic" doses of LSD for phantom limb pain in a partially blinded study. Suffering from phantom limb pain is a well-known phenomenon for humans who have had a limb amputated. These patients still feel pain where the limb would have been. The cause of this sometimes severe pain is unknown, but it has been associated with the serotonin neurotransmitter system. The patients received daily intravenous doses of 25 µg LSD for the first week and then doses of 50 μg LSD for the next two weeks. The patients received the drug at 9:00am and were questioned every day about their sensations. The daily use of analgesics was also measured. After three weeks of LSD treatment, placebo was administered for four weeks. No psychic reactions were detected with the 25 μg dose, but four patients had perceptual distortions during the first two days of treatment with the 50 μg dose. In five patients, LSD produced improvement of pain and reduction of analgesic use. In two patients, the effect was striking and they could cope without using analgesics. In the other patients the pain was moderately reduced and the use of analgetics reduced by about 50%. In two patients the treatment was ineffective.

Effects on psychiatric shock treatment

Bente et al. (1957) referred to the observation that treatments with insulin coma therapy and electroshock therapy (used to treat psychiatric disorders at the time) leads to slowing of the spontaneous cerebral rhythms in the EEG. The authors studied the influence of LSD (20–150 μg i.v.) on this phenomenon. Results showed that premedication with LSD (even at the lowest dosage) inhibits the development of slow waves. This is similar to reactions from other premedications such as barbiturates or neuroleptic drugs.

8

The Pharmacology of LSD

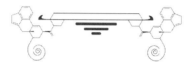

Since the accidental discovery in 1943 of the extraordinary psychological changes produced by LSD, an extensive literature has built up dealing with LSD's effects in animals and man. It is beyond the scope of this outline to provide a detailed overview of this research activity, which we have done elsewhere (Passie et al. 2008, Hintzen & Passie 2010). I will describe a few basic facts that may be relevant for the use of low-dose LSD and microdosing.

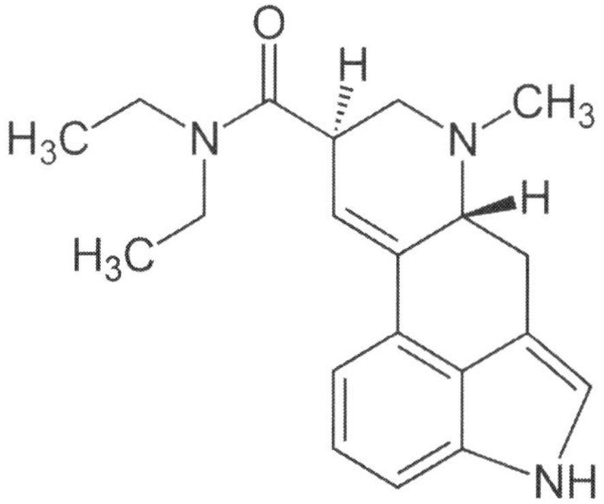

Figure 4: Chemical structure of lysergic acid diethylamide (LSD)

Absorption, distribution and metabolism

LSD is water-soluble as a salt (tartrate) and is highly active if taken by mouth. LSD is thought to be quickly and completely absorbed in the intestinal tract.

Investigations on the distribution of LSD in the body reveal that intravenously administered LSD does not disperse very rapidly from the blood and takes a timespan of 10–30 minutes to be distributed into the tissue of different organs. In the course of metabolism in the liver, LSD can be transformed into several inactive metabolites, which are closely related chemically to LSD. The most important metabolite is 2-oxo-3-hydroxy-lysergic acid diethylamide (OH-LSD), which is not psychoactive. In healthy human subjects, approximately 1–2% of an orally administered dose of LSD was eliminated in unchanged form in the urine within 24 hours and 13% was eliminated as OH-LSD (Dolder et al. 2015). A few hours after administration, the greatest portion of radioactively-labelled LSD and its metabolites are found in the content of the intestinal tract.

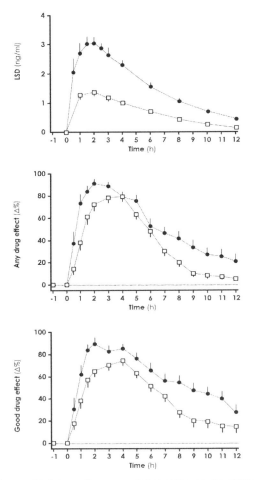

Diagram 21: Schematic representation of the course of blood plasma levels of LSD and its subjective effects (Dolder et al. 2017)

Upshall and Wailling (1972) have demonstrated that with a large meal, plasma concentrations of orally ingested LSD were half as much as on an empty stomach. When a smaller meal was eaten, plasma levels were somewhere intermediate. As shown in Diagram 21, the subjective, cognitive, and sympathomimetic effects of oral LSD closely matched the time-course of LSD concentrations in plasma as shown in Diagram 21 (Dolder et al. 2017).

The distribution of LSD across tissue and organ systems has yet to be quantified for the human organism. The presence of considerable amounts of the drug in the brain and cerebrospinal fluid (CSF) of rats and cats indicates that LSD may easily pass the blood–brain barrier. In monkeys *(Macaca mulatta)* the maximum LSD level in CSF was reached within 10 minutes after intravenous administration, and fell during the subsequent hours (Axelrod et al. 1957).

Pharmacokinetics

Pharmacokinetics describes what happens to a substance in the body. Plasma levels after the oral administration of LSD were first described by Aghajanian and Bing (1962) in five healthy males for up to 8 hours after administration, and recently confirmed in larger studies in healthy males and females by Dolder et al. (2015, 2017). As shown in Diagram 21, the rise and decline of the plasma levels follows linear pharmacokinetics. After oral administration, maximal plasma levels are reached after a mean time of 1.5 hours. Subjective effects peak at a mean time of 2.5 hours after drug administration. The average elimination half-life of LSD is 2.6 hours.

Concentrations of LSD in blood plasma are largely congruent with the intensity and course of the subjective effects (Diagram 22). Thus, the acute subjective effects of LSD last as long as LSD can be detected in the circulation and the intensity of the subjective effects of LSD correlates well with its concentration in the blood plasma.

After an oral intake of 100 μg of LSD tartrate, LSD and in particular OH-LSD and other metabolites are detectable up to 34–120 hours in human urine (Peel & Boynton 1980). Each doubling of the initial dosage will add about 5 hours to the detection time (Papaz & Foltz 1990).

Leuner's (1962) meticulous clinical observations in the early 1960s revealed a course of effects suggesting two distinct phases of subjective action, with a change occurring at the mid-point of the duration of action

(Leuner 1962). This observation, which was based on the observation of a few hundred administrations of LSD to humans, was supported by pharmacological studies in animals more than 40 years later. Marona-Lewicka et al. (2005) found the behavioural effects of LSD in rats to occur in two different temporal phases: an initial suppression of the usual exploratory behaviour, followed by an increase of locomotor activity of the animals. The authors suggest that the first temporal phase is mainly meditated by LSD's interaction with serotonin receptors, whereas the second phase is mediated by D2 dopamine receptor stimulation. However, several recent studies have so far not confirmed different phases of the subjective effects of LSD (Schmid et al. 2015, Dolder et al. 2016, Carhart-Harris et al. 2016, Preller et al. 2017). Additionally, the 5-HT2A receptor antagonist ketanserin almost completely prevented all effects of LSD indicating that the subjective response is largely mediated via action at the 5-HT2A receptors (Preller et al. 2017).

Doses and effects

The original first dose of LSD intentionally taken by Albert Hofmann in 1943 was 250 µg of LSD tartrate, although the effective oral dose later proved to be 0.5–2.0 µg per kg bodyweight. Amounts of 25 µg are known to induce discernible effects in most humans. Diagram 23 shows the dose levels of LSD as used for different purposes.

After 100–250 µg LSD (free base), psychological and sympathomimetic effects reach their peak after 1.5–2.5 hours. The half-life of LSD is 2.5–3 hours (Dolder et al. 2016, Aghajanian & Bing 1964). In a recent clinical study Dolder et al. (2017) found that the full spectrum of LSD's effects, including psychological and somatic changes, is reached with a dose of 200 µg of free base by mouth. A 200 µg dose produced overall significantly greater alterations of mind than a 100 µg dose (Liechti et al. 2017). By far most of the studies in the past have used a dose range of 1–2 µg per kg bodyweight (roughly equivalent to 50–200 µg) by mouth. However, many studies, especially if they were concerned with "psychedelic therapy" or induced "experimental psychoses" have also used higher doses of 250–500 µg per os. Dolder et al. (2017) found the mean effect duration to be 8.2 hours (range 5.0–14) and 11.2 hours (range: 6.4–19) after administration of 100 and 200 µg, respectively. It is important to note that lower doses lead to a shorter duration of action (Diagram 2) consistent with the pharmacokinetics of LSD.

With a dose of 30–50 µg the effect duration is 4–6 hours (e.g. Leuner 1962, Abramson et al. 1955d, Stoll 1947). Diagram 22 presents the course of LSD blood plasma levels with different dosages.

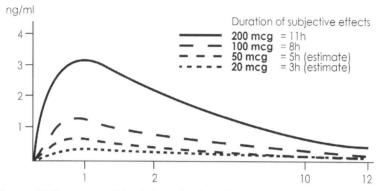

Diagram 22: Time course of blood plasma levels of LSD after administration of doses of 200, 100, and 50 µg per os of the free base. The plasma levels for the 100 and 200 µg dose were taken from Dolder et al. (2017). The course of blood plasma levels for the 50 and 20 µg dose were estimated. Duration of effects with lower doses were estimated based on data by Dolder et al. (2017).

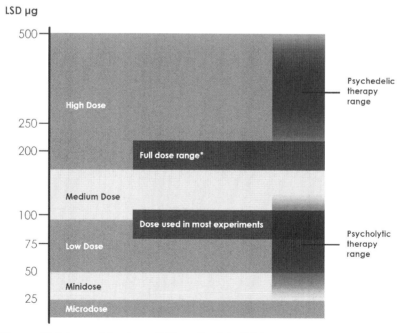

Diagram 23: Scheme of the doses of LSD used in clinical trials
*According to data of Dolder et al. (2017)

Diagram 23 provides an overview of the different doses as given in clinical trials with LSD. A table from Hollister's book (1968) illustrates the range of symptoms experienced by subjects under the influence of a dose of 75–100 µg of LSD tartrate (Table 12).

	Linton/Langs	Hollister
	100 µg	1 µg/kg
Somatic		
Dizziness	X	X
Weakness, difficulty moving	X	X
Hot or cold feeling	X	X
Nausea	X	X
Numbness, paresthesias	X	X
Body lighter or heavier	X	X
Shaking of body		X
Drowsiness		X
Appetite decreased		X
Ill feeling		X
Dry mouth		X
Perceptual		
Altered shapes, colours	X	X
Blurred vision		X
Visual contrasts clearer		X
Hearing more acute		X
Body looked strange	X	
Psychological		
Altered mood		
Distorted, slowed subjective time	X	X
Difficulty expressing thoughts	X	X
Depersonalization	X	X
Dreamlike state	X	X
Loss of control of thoughts, feelings	X	X
Difficulty in concentration	X	
Poor memory and retention	X	
Impaired judgement	X	
Rapid or recurrent thoughts	X	
Visual hallucinations	X	X

Table 12: Most frequently positively answered questionnaire items in two studies of LSD (from Hollister 1968)

In addition to psychological phenomena, LSD (100-200 µg) produces moderate sympathomimetic effects as reflected in vital sign changes such as increased pulse rate (+10–15 bpm) and blood pressure (+10–15 mm Hg systolic), slight increase in body temperature (0.3–0.5 °C), mydriasis, slight blood sugar elevation, and additional symptoms such as headache, lack of appetite, dry mouth, nausea, tremor, and muscular weakness (Dolder et al. 2016). All these symptoms are mild and vary widely between individuals, with mydriasis being the most consistently detected symptom. Respiration remains unchanged (Passie et al. 2008).

In a study to explore effects of LSD on creativity, Zegane et al. (1967) generated the only data that have been published on blood pressure and pulse at a dose of 0.5 µg/kg per os (Table 13). Their results show a slight rise of blood pressure during the experiment, but a slowing of pulse rate. Studies are currently testing the subjective and autonomic effects of 25 and 50 µg in healthy subjects, but data are not yet published.

	LSD	Placebo
Number of Subjects	20	11
Blood Pressure (mean)	+4.95	-6.91
Pulse (mean)	-1.26	-6.37

Table 13: Physiological changes with a 0.5 µg/kg dose of LSD per os (Zegans et al. 1967)

In an early research study, Rawnsley and Anderson (1954: 53) stated that "... over certain minimal doses there is no clear-cut relationship either qualitative or quantitative between the clinical picture and the amount of substance taken". In contrast, Abramson et al. (1955e) found with their questionnaire that with an increase in dose (0–225 µg LSD), the number and subjective severity of symptoms increase. Isbell et al. (1956) have confirmed the results of Abramson. In a study on different doses of LSD, Klee et al. (1961) found a considerable variation in the effects of the same dose in different individuals, but relatively consistent effects when the same dose was repeatedly given to the same subject.

Actions on receptors

LSD binds to human serotonin (5-HT) receptor subtypes (5-HT1A, 5-HT2A, 5-HT2B, 5-HT2C), as well as several others. It also activates the dopamine receptor subtypes D1, D2, D3, and D4 as well as α1 and α2 adrenergic receptors (Nichols 2016, Rickli et al 2016). The primary action of LSD at the receptor level is the activation of the 5-HT2A receptor and the processes that follow its activation. If this receptor is blocked, no hallucinogenic effects appear after LSD (Preller et al. 2017).

From a technical point of view, LSD is probably best called a mixed 5-HT2/5-HT1 receptor partial agonist, especially on those receptors expressed on neocortical pyramidal cells (Nichols 2016). Beside the direct effects on pyramidal cells, activation of 5-HT2A receptors also leads to increased cortical glutamate levels (Winter et al. 2004). Recent research has shown that the serotonin 5-HT2B receptor (very similar to the 5-HT2A receptor) has a conformation that has a "lid" (named "extracellular loop 2" or EL2) that "locks" the LSD molecule inside the receptor (Figure 5). This might explain the very potent action of LSD. According to Nichols (2018), when LSD is administered it takes about 3 hours to equilibrate into the receptor, and then 8-10 hours to come back off. Nichols et al. (2018) have synthesized numerous LSD analogues, where the diethylamide side chain has been modified, but none of them had the typical effects of LSD.

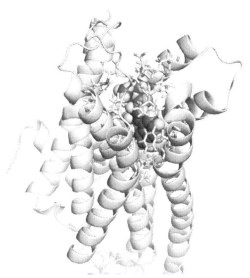

Figure 5: This figure is a PyMol rendering of the crystal structure of LSD bound within the serotonin 5-HT2B receptor, as published by Wacker et al. (2017), courtesy of Dr David E. Nichols

Another important aspect of the mechanism of action of LSD is the fact that agonist molecules for different receptors activate a cascade of actions inside brain cells. These are called second and third messenger systems. If they are activated, a further chain of reactions starts up inside the cells. However, all of the signalling pathways that are or might be activated to mediate LSD's effects have not been conclusively elucidated (Nichols 2016). Important effects are exerted on β-arrestin signalling and glutamate levels in the brain (Liechti 2017). However, indoleamine hallucinogens like LSD and psilocybin not only activate 5-HT2 receptors but bind to many other monoamine receptors and it is possible that their interactions with these receptors modulate their overall effects in humans.

With a dose of 100 μg LSD free base given by mouth, plasma concentration (Cmax) of 1.3 ng/ml or approximately 4 nM has been measured (Dolder et al. 2017). This plasma concentration is in the range of the binding affinity (ki Value) of LSD to the 5-HT2A receptor (0.5–10 nM depending on study). Thus, with an LSD dose of 100 μg, high enough brain concentrations can be expected to allow for a half maximal occupation of 5-HT2A receptors in the brain, and associated functional consequences. Consistently, pharmacokinetic-pharmacodynamic studies found an EC50 value for the overall effect of LSD of approximately 1 ng/mL. That means that at a plasma concentration of approximately 1 ng/mL of LSD, half of its maximal possible response is observed. This concentration is slightly below the peak concentration of LSD after administration of a 100 *μg* dose. Although this has not been tested yet, the available pharmacokinetic-pharmacodynamic studies (Dolder et al. 2017) indicate that at a 50 and 25 *μg* dose approximately 20–30% and 10–15% of the maximum responses are reached, respectively. Dolder et al. (2015, 2017) have shown that LSD follows typical linear pharmacokinetics. Given this, a linear relation between dose and plasma level (Area under curve, AUC) can be expected with lower doses.

The estimated plasma level for a half-maximal receptor occupation (when Cmax is equal at the synaptic cleft and the affinity to the receptor is around 1nM) would be around 0.3 ng LSD per millilitre of blood plasma. However, caution is advised, because concentrations in blood plasma and brain tissue are dependent on a substance's kinetic properties, and are rarely identical. Therefore, estimates on the magnitude of receptor occupation with doses of 20 and 50 μg might well be speculative, but it appears possible that receptor occupation is in the 10–20% range. No data exists on the functional consequences of receptor stimulation at this magnitude.

The aforementioned data and estimates show that lower doses cause less activity. Beside the fact that a certain plasma level is needed to induce detectable effects, lower activity might result from the fact that a certain concentration of LSD within the blood plasma has to be reached in order to pass through the blood-brain barrier (BBB). The BBB is an additional layer (in comparison to blood vessels in other tissues or organs) which surrounds all blood vessels in the brain. This layer contains active and passive transport mechanisms, which promote or prohibit the transport of a drug through the blood vessels' membranes into brain tissue. It is well known that some substances need to reach a certain plasma level to activate the appropriate transport mechanisms to pass the BBB to reach the brain's receptors to cause an effect. As LSD needs 20–30 minutes to reveal its effects after intravenous administration (Hoch 1956, Carhart-Harris et al. 2016a), it is likely that a substance has to reach a certain plasma level to cross the BBB. The behaviour at the BBB could be an explanation for the slow onset of LSD effects after intravenous application. This is in contrast to psilocybin and dimethyltryptamine (DMT) where effects are immediate (Hasler et al. 1997, Strassman et al. 1994). We do not know precisely what level would be sufficient for LSD to begin to cross the BBB, but this may have implications when considering microdosing. It is also possible, however, that this delay of onset of effect could be related to the relatively slow receptor association rate of LSD for the 5-HT2A receptor (Wacker et al. 2017). Another factor could be the pattern of the time course of distribution of LSD in the human organism. As with other pharmaceuticals, it is probable that LSD is distributed from the blood plasma into different tissues with different affinity and speed. In addition, when the concentration in the blood plasma decreases, it may flow back from the tissue into the blood and might reach other tissues from there. No data about these distribution processes with LSD or any other hallucinogens exist at present.

Given that pharmacokinetic and pharmacodynamic data on microdosing have not been established, any consideration about receptor occupancy after sub-hallucinogenic doses is speculative. Studies using Positron Emission Tomography (PET) are needed to establish receptor occupation at different dose levels. With this method it is possible to establish the level of receptor occupancy through the use of positron-emitting radioactively labelled LSD molecules (or other ligands that may be displaced after LSD administration) in the living human brain.

Endocrinological effects

During its acute effects, LSD increases plasma concentrations of cortisol, prolactin, oxytocin, and epinephrine. LSD has no influence on norepinephrine testosterone, or progesterone (Schmid et al. 2015, Strajhar et al. 2016).

Neurophysiological effects

The main mechanism by which LSD exerts its effects is the activation of the 5-HT2A receptor, especially on pyramidal cells in the frontal cortex. This activation leads to an activation of glutamate transmission in the frontal cortex, which results in downstream modulatory effects in subcortical areas. This modulation might influence gating functions for sensory and cognitive processing. Martin et al. (2015) have detected a subgroup of cells deep in the prefrontal cortex of rodents that are acutely responsive to psychedelics, and express higher levels of 5-HT2A receptors than other cortical cells. These cells, which may be in the claustrum, send glutamate projects to higher cortical areas. Martin et al. (2015) have called these cells the "trigger population".

The EEG shows mild and few specific signs of activation after LSD ingestion. Most common is an increase in mean alpha frequency (e.g. Elkes et al. 1954).

With respect to alterations of brain metabolism, the major hallucinogens activate the right hemisphere, influence thalamic functioning, and increase metabolism in paralimbic structures as well as the frontal cortex. In regard to global brain metabolism, some investigators found an increased metabolism (Vollenweider et al. 1997, Hermle et al. 1992), but others found no change (Gouzoulis-Mayfrank et al. 1999, Riba et al. 2006).

As recent studies with functional Magnetic Resonance Imaging (fMRI) have shown, LSD alters the functional integrity of the brain networks and the separation between networks. LSD-induced disintegration of the so-called Default Mode Network (DMN) (Carhart-Harris et al. 2016; Müller et al. 2018), which is activated when a person is calm and without any interferences from the environment, correlated with ratings of ego dissolution (Carhart-Harris et al, 2016). At the whole-brain level, LSD increased functional connectivity between various brain regions (Carhart-Harris et al. 2016, Müller et al. 2018, Müller et al. 2017). LSD globally decreased within-network integrity. In sum, these findings indicate increased global network connectivity within the brain and a reduction of network separation. In the usual dose range (100–200 µg), LSD enhances activity in areas of the brain that are associated with self-referential cognition and processing (e.g. Preller et al. 2017). LSD also reduces the activity in the brains "fear centre", the amygdala, if the setting is appropriate (Mueller et al. 2017).

However, as Liechti (2017) has pointed out in a recent review of LSD research, much data has been derived from very few small studies. Therefore, chance findings should be expected, especially in respect to fMRI data on functional connectivity.

Toxicity

The toxicity of LSD varies widely across species, with the rabbit particularly sensitive. Toxicity seems to correlate better with brain weight than with body weight as shown in Table 14. Klee et al. (1961) found that physiological changes were most intense at the highest dose used (1,120 µg per 70 kg subject), with some hypertension.

The lethal dose (LD 50) in man was calculated to be 0.2 mg per kg bodyweight or 14,000 µg (Hoffer and Osmond 1967: 95). However, the lethal dose in humans is unknown as a case was documented where eight individuals insufflated a very large amount (in the range of 100–200 mg, which implies a 1,000-fold overdose!) by confusing pure LSD with cocaine. They suffered from comatose states, rise in body temperature, vomiting, light gastric bleeding, and respiratory problems. However, all survived with rapid hospital treatment and without residual effects (Klock et al. 1974). Up to the present day there is no documented case in which the physiological effects of LSD alone led to death (Nichols & Grob 2018).

Researchers in the past have excluded subjects with illnesses like epilepsy, grave diseases of heart, liver or kidney as well as psychosis from their studies (cf. Hintzen & Passie 2010).

Animal	Body-weight (kg)	LD50 (mg/kg)	Brain weight (gr.)
Mouse	0.035	46 (i.v.)	0.5
Rat	0.5	16.5 (i.v.)	1.7
Rabbit	3.5	0.3 (i.v.)	85
Man	75	10 (p.o.)	1400

Table 14: Toxicity of LSD. LD_{50} is the dose at which half of the animals will die.

Daily long-term use of LSD

In respect to the development of tolerance with repeated administration of psychedelics, the reader is referred to Chapter 11 which covers this topic extensively.

Rats have been given LSD daily in doses of 2.5 mg/kg for periods of up to a month without cumulative effect or any lasting damage. Since the maximal tolerable single dose in the rat is 3.2 mg/kg, no cumulative factors seem to be present. No tolerance appears to develop with a daily regimen of administration in that animals pretreated with LSD require the same LD_{100} (a dose from which all animals will die) as untreated animals. However, the somatic symptoms induced by LSD in the animals such as tremor, increased reflex response, and pilomotor erection, decline in intensity within a few days and the animals lost significant weight in comparison to untreated animals.

Human adults have been given LSD (100–150 μg) for periods of 77 days without detectable damage (Sankar 1975, Isbell et al. 1956). Schizophrenic and autistic children have been treated with daily doses of LSD (100–250 μg) for up to 35 months without any obvious damage (Bender & Sankar 1968). However, the examinations and methods used at the time might not have been sensitive enough to detect possible damage.

Addictive properties

LSD is not addictive, despite the fact that some cases of very regular LSD users are described in the literature during the heyday of LSD use in the late 1960s (Blacker et al. 1968). The usual animal experiments used to detect addictive properties of a substance do not show any addictive potential for LSD. Animals will not "press the button to get the drug" again after the first administration. In contrast, when cocaine is provided, animals self-administer the drug until they develop seizures.

Ungerleider and Fisher (1967) and Kihlbohm et al. (1967) concluded from clinical evidence that addiction was not reported, only increased tolerance and habituation. In addition, there is no withdrawal syndrome when a person stops taking LSD after extended periods of daily use (Isbell et al. 1956).

Possible complications and long-term consequences of LSD

Whilst several positive psychological consequences of taking LSD/psilocybin in carefully supervised situations are shown in some methodologically sound studies (e.g. McGothlin et al. 1967, MacLean et al. 2011), serious damage can result from ingestion of LSD in uncontrolled circumstances or by vulnerable individuals. Possible complications during the acute effects of the drug range from mild anxiety attacks to panic and delusional thinking, as well as psychological lability and psychotiform experiences and behaviour. Although the risk of dangerous behaviour under the influence of the drug is hard to calculate, the long-term risks experienced in some cases consist mainly of prolonged anxiety, trauma through "bad trips", and so-called flashbacks. Flashbacks are defined as recurrences of fragments of the experience, which were first experienced under the drug's influence. These phenomena are sometimes experienced as enjoyable "gratis trips", but might also result from traumatic "horror trips" and be disagreeable. However, flashbacks tend to be experienced only occasionally, last a few seconds, and disappear within a few weeks (for a review see Holland & Passie 2011 and Halpern et al. 2016). From a logical point of view it can be said that the major complications that can result from the intake of medium or high doses of LSD will be significantly reduced if low or very low doses of the substance are used. Most of the potential complications simply do not appear with the use of low doses. However, with doses in the range of 25–50 µg some deficits in performance (e.g. driving, behaviour in complex social or stressful situations) might be present, and put the user at risk. There is also a risk of inducing anxiety and psychological labilization, as has sometimes been reported even with doses of 10–15 µg LSD (cf. Fadiman 2016: 57).

9

Research on Tolerance to LSD

Tolerance is defined as a decrease in responsiveness of the organism to a drug after repeated administration. A good example is the daily drinking of alcohol, which after some weeks of daily use induces tolerance, meaning that a regular drinker must drink much more than a non-drinker to get the same effects. With most drugs, this adaptive process usually takes weeks or months. Tolerance occurs much more rapidly with LSD, however. In fact, if LSD is taken twice a day (e.g. at 9:00 am and 9:00 pm) humans will be completely tolerant to its autonomic and psychological effects after just two days. This rapid development of tolerance is called *tachyphylasis*. In contrast to a substance such as alcohol, however, if humans have reached a state of tolerance to LSD, they will not show any reaction, even to a three-fold higher dose (Isbell et al. 1956). Abramson et al. (1956) gave 100 µg LSD for 3–6 days to healthy volunteers and demonstrated that after 2–3 days a solid tolerance developed. After tolerance to LSD is achieved and placebo instead of LSD is given for the next 3 days, typical LSD effects will recur upon dosing with LSD on the fourth day (Isbell et al. 1956). Hoffer and Osmond (1967) have demonstrated that a first dose of 100 µg LSD produces an intense experience in 80% of subjects. The same dose taken the next day will produce a much milder reaction and, if repeated, on the third day produces no reaction. With a steady increase of dosage (day 1: 100 µg, day 2: 200 µg, day 3: 300 µg, day 4: 400 µg and day 5: 500 µg) clear changes in behaviour were evident on the first day. On the next day, only a few changes could be observed, and on the third and fourth days none at all. With the fifth and last dose of 500 µg virtually no reaction to the substance was seen (Cholden 1955). Through variation of the intervals of LSD-free days, it was found that it takes a period of 3–5 days abstinence to re-establish the original effects of the drug (Isbell et al. 1956).

It is not quite clear just how far a dosing scheme with one dose per day will consistently induce tolerance, as there are differing results in the literature. Some researchers did not find significant tolerance with one daily dose (e.g. Jonas and Downer 1964), whereas those who dosed their subjects every 12 hours found definite tolerance (e.g. Isbell 1956). Freedman et al. (1964) found that tolerance in rats develops after 7–8 days with a single daily dose. This time became shorter when the LSD was administered more often (Buchborn et al. 2016). Buchborn et al. (2014) have demonstrated tolerance development in rats with two daily doses of LSD, but no tolerance with one dose per day.

Cross-tolerance is defined as occurring when tolerance to a certain substance has been developed by the organism, which also induces tolerance to a similar drug. For example, LSD is known to cause a cross-tolerance to psilocybin and mescaline (Abramson et al. 1956).

It has been shown that tolerance to LSD develops rapidly in humans whereas tolerance to mescaline develops less rapidly and is less complete (Cholden 1955). Humans tolerant to LSD were very resistant to mescaline, while the reverse situation did not occur to the same degree. However, although tolerance to the psychological effects of LSD occurs, no tolerance develops with respect to pulse rate and temperature changes (cf. Hintzen & Passie 2010). LSD induces a complete tolerance to psilocybin (Isbell et al. 1956, Abramson et al. (1960b). No cross-tolerance to LSD or psilocybin develops in any direction with tetrahydrocannabinol, amphetamine, or the opioids (Hintzen & Passie 2010).

With respect to development of tolerance when taking low doses of LSD, it is worth mentioning that at lower doses there is a shorter time period at which the blood—or tissue—concentration of the drug is above that which would be sufficient to activate the receptors. It is known from research studies that the duration of action of LSD is much shorter with lower doses (e.g. 25–50 µg). The usual duration of LSD's effects (with a 100–200 µg dose) is 7–9 hours (Dolder et al. 2017), decreasing to 4–5 hours with lower doses (Leuner 1962, Abramson 1955d). Therefore, it is very probable that the time period of a "significant interaction" of very low doses with the human organism might be even shorter, perhaps in the range of only 3–5 hours (Leuner 1962, Abramson et al. 1955d). Presumably, this is caused by the fact that LSD tissue levels are only above the threshold for perceptible LSD effects for a shorter time period.

There are a few anecdotal reports, which suggest there is no development of tolerance with (even daily) microdosing. For example, Copley (1962), did not experience tolerance during six weeks of microdosing with mescaline (50 mg). In contrast, there is consistent evidence that even doses as low as 50 µg LSD lead to tolerance (e.g. Isbell et al. 1956, Abramson et al. 1956).

Mechanisms of tolerance

The development of tolerance to LSD is caused by interaction of the drug with the human organism at the receptor level. The principal serotonin receptor subtype with which LSD interacts is the 5-HT2A receptor. With chronic exposure to the drug this receptor becomes "internalized", i.e. goes from residing within the neuronal cell membrane into the interior of the cell (Buchborn et al. 2016). The drug in the aqueous extracellular milieu is then no longer able to engage the receptor to produce an effect. Experiments with rats (130 µg/kg LSD i.v. for five consecutive days) indicated a decrease in 5-HT2A receptor signalling caused by a reduction of 5-HT2A receptor density and reduced second messenger induction (via G-protein coupling) (Gresch et al. 2005). It also seems probable that the receptor might later be destroyed. In addition, the biosynthesis of new receptor protein is inhibited (Buchborn et al. 2016). Another possible mechanism is the desensitization of processes occurring as a functional output of the activation of the 5-HT2A receptor. Relevant to this point, recent research indicates that the development of tolerance to LSD alternatively involves the minimization of the 5-HT2A receptor-mediated response of the glutamate system, and is not entirely due to the downregulation of 5-HT2A receptors. When LSD is administered repeatedly, glutamate receptor binding sites are also downregulated. That is most likely an indirect effect because LSD does not directly bind to the glutamate receptor (Buchborn et al. 2014).

On the chronic ingestion of LSD

The daily ingestion of LSD is promulgated by some microdosers. In one older study, with a daily dose of 100 µg of LSD, it appears that taking LSD for weeks or even months does not seem to result in obvious damage (Bender & Sankar 1968). However, this might be due either to the development of tolerance or lack of sensitivity of the instruments/measures used at the time to detect unwanted effects. Despite becoming tolerant to the more obvious effects of LSD, it seems unwise to take LSD—even at low doses—over longer periods of time. This is because the adaption of the human organism to the exposure of certain substances is a complex matter. Even if the obvious effects are no longer felt, the organism might cope with the impact of the substance by altering the metabolism or turnover rate of various endogenous substances (e.g. serotonin, dopamine) as well as causing changes of the receptors; not just in the brain, as it is likely, but in other physiological systems that might also be affected (e.g. blood platelets are altered by serotonin-active drugs). Another example is given by Sankar, who demonstrated that daily dosing with LSD for eight weeks led to a rise of inorganic phosphate in the blood. However, this rise increased at a slower rate with further applications of LSD (Sankar 1975).

More recently it was demonstrated that daily administration of LSD to rats for four weeks leads to alterations of gene expression profiles. These changes were found even four weeks after the LSD administration was stopped. The genes altered were relevant for neurotransmission (Drd2, Gabrb1), synaptic plasticity (Nr2a, Krox20), energy metabolism (Atp5d, Ndufa1) and neuropeptide signalling (Npy, Bdnf), among others (Martin et al. 2014). It should be noted that the relevance of these changes in gene expression on the animal or human organism are still unclear. However, using LSD in animal models for schizophrenia, a significant psychiatric disease, have shown that daily administration of doses of 160 µg LSD per kg body weight (equivalent to a dose of 12,000 µg for a 75 kg human) for three months leads to a behavioural state characterized by hyperactivity and hyperirritability, increased locomotor activity, anhedonia, and impairment of social interaction. After the administration of LSD was stopped, these changes persisted at the same magnitude as they were under the drug, for a period of three months (Marona-Lewicka et al. 2011). The authors have suggested that these changes are due to a mechanism involving the above-named changes in gene expression. In view of the very high LSD dose used in these studies, it is at best unclear how far these "adaptive changes" are relevant to the use of moderate or low doses in humans. The fact that the behavioural or obvious physiological changes as perceived in these animal experiments (with high doses) were not seen in humans who received a single dose of 100 µg LSD once daily for up to six months (Bender & Sankar 1968), is suggestive of another pattern of reaction with lower doses in humans.

It should be noted that it is unknown how far alterations in sleep and dreams after LSD administration (which occur in very low doses, cf. Chapter 8) are affected by the development of tolerance.

Can the development of tolerance be prevented by specific dosing?

What happens if one "prevents" the development of tolerance to LSD by only using it every third day? It can be presumed from the results of the tolerance studies, that tolerance will not develop if such a dosing strategy is used (e.g. Isbell et al. 1956). The most solid tolerance develops if LSD is given twice daily, somewhat less so if given once a day. Unfortunately, there are no studies to date that have studied a "one dose every three days" regimen (cf. Hintzen & Passie 2010), so we are not able to predict how the human organism will react to such a dosing regimen. One should be aware that most of the mechanisms by which the organism becomes tolerant to LSD might be activated when one is dosing every third day for longer time periods, like weeks or months. This general statement does not say much as we don't know what will happen, as there are no scientific studies regarding this. However, there are a lot of cases reported (Fadiman, personal communication, 2018) of people taking microdoses in both three and two day regimens over months with no reports of tolerance, and many reports of noticing a distinct shift on the third day—characterized by a more favourable state before taking the next dose.

If a substance is taken regularly/repeatedly over a period of weeks, months or even years without longer breaks (few weeks or more), its administration can be considered chronic. This would also apply for a microdosing regimen a la Fadiman (a dose every third day). Based on rat experiments by Martin et al. (2014), with an every-other-day LSD intake over periods of months, it can be assumed that a long-term application of LSD exerts significant effects on behaviour and brain gene expression. Although the doses used in this study are far beyond those seen with human (micro)doses, the observed effects are likely due to LSD's interaction with monoamine receptors. Thus, in case microdoses as 10–20 µg lead to a significant receptor occupation at 5-HT2A or other LSD-binding proteins, microdoses might be expected to induce physiological adaptations (such as tolerance or sensitization) over time as well. Whether these changes are "good" or "bad" depends on the system which expresses the given monoamine receptor, and on the system's respective pre-drug state. A psychological loosening when in a condition of excessive rigidity (e.g., in depressive states) might be beneficial, on the other hand an alteration of a previously healthy cardiovascular, hepatic, or renal system might not (Buchborn 2018). The expression of 5-HT2A receptors, as well as other LSD-binding proteins, is certainly not restricted to the brain; other systems might likewise show adaptations analogous to those found by Martin et al. (2014) in rat brains. Microdosing studies might therefore be well-advised to take both psychological and physiological parameters under scrutiny.

10

Microdosing and Placebos

There is probably no other phenomenon that better reflects the inseparable interaction between psychological and somatic factors than the placebo effect. This phenomenon is a complex psychobiological process consisting of learning and expectancy components acting on neurophysiological systems. Its efficacy has been proven empirically in a range of fields, including pain management and the immune system.

Although the word "placebo" translated means "I shall please", the word in medicine generally involves the concept that a relatively pharmacologically inert substance is given to a patient for experiments designed to test the activity of another drug (it can also be used to refer to a treatment which is not centred around 'taking medicine', thus there is for example, placebo surgery).

Inactive or virtually inactive substances can trigger what are known as 'placebo effects', and these effects also contribute to the response of effective treatment. Our knowledge about the mechanisms that produce placebo effects has much expanded during the last decades. For example endorphin release can be triggered by cognitive mechanisms (Colloca et al. 2013). However, research was not able to characterize a "placebo-responder's personality pattern" consistently, which points to the complexity of the matter. Finniss et al. (2010) have described 12 different possible mechanisms of placebo effects. Nevertheless, a specific mechanism is not always detectable. Expectancy, prior experience, classical conditioning, suggestibility and verbal suggestion as well as the actual emotional state are some major determinants of the placebo effect. Two main mechanisms involve unconscious Pavlovian conditioning and cognitive expectations, whereby the subject anticipates treatment outcome (Benedetti 2008). A placebo treatment, along with the whole psychosocial context surrounding the therapeutic act, exerts a powerful effect on the central nervous system, modulating neuronal activity and triggering the release of endogenous substances acting on specific targets. Expectations can be raised in several ways, one of the most powerful being verbal suggestions. In 2008, a hugely impactful article by Kirsch et al. (2008) pointed to the fact that most of the "effects" from antidepressant drugs are based on placebo effects.

It is important to be aware of possible placebo effects, especially when it comes to potentially active substances where subjective effects are not easy or even impossible to detect and calculate. This is the case with very low doses of LSD or psilocybin, etc.

Placebo responses are not confined to the medical domain. For example, they have also been studied in physical performance, where the administration of sham (=pseudo) ergogenic supplements (or procedures) induced improvements of muscle work and decrease of muscle fatigue perception. Interestingly, negative expectations produced the opposite effects (Benedetti 2008).

To illustrate this, an example experiment is presented here, which was conducted to measure work and fatigue in healthy subjects undergoing strenuous exercise. Examined were the effects of a sham caffeine drink as a placebo and different verbal suggestions/instructions. No caffeine, alcohol, or any other drug was ingested for 48 hours beforehand. 110 students got a light breakfast on the morning of the experiment. During the study only placebo doses of caffeine were administered (<1% of an active dose). The view and taste of the (decaffeinated) coffee suggested that this was a full dose of caffeinated coffee. Four groups were given different information: 1. "no caffeine", 2. "might be caffeine at a chance of 50% or 25%" or 3. "Only the control group received a full dose of caffeine". The fourth placebo group were not given any instruction. Experimental subjects had to extend their legs against a leg extensor device lifting a weight of 15 kg with 5 kg increments, until they were unable to continue the task. When the experiment began, subjects performed the leg extension task to voluntary fatigue, until complete exhaustion. The results of the placebo group were compared to another group which was given the same instructions, but openly told that the beverage did not contain any ergogenic substance. This group did not show any additional effect compared to the trials without the beverage. If the persons were told that they had a 50% chance of getting caffeine, they showed significantly better results (+20%) on the exercise. If they were told that they had only a 25% chance of getting caffeine, the group did not show any difference (Carlino et al. 2014). This effect might be different when a patient is under the influence of pain or anxiety.

It is noteworthy that many of the effects which experimental subjects feel under the effects of an inactive placebo are very similar to those of low doses of LSD, as established, for example, by the comprehensive tests of the Abramson group (cf. Table 15). These effects include; nausea, feeling of heaviness, difficulty in concentrating, feeling of weakness, lightness of body, slight talkativeness, tiredness, headache, and dizziness. These similarities cause serious difficulties when differentiating placebo responses from effects of the "real drug". However, one difference was shown in respect to the course of the claimed symptoms. While the placebo response was detected relatively continuously over the whole experiment, the LSD responses (with 50–100 µg) were found mainly during the first 1.5–2.5 hours (Abramson et al. 1955, Linton & Langs 1962).

In 1969, Büttner conducted a study on placebo effects within an LSD experiment on healthy volunteers (n = 10, age 22–31). No one in the study had experienced LSD before. 1.3–1.8 µg/kg LSD or placebo was given by mouth, but no one was informed that a placebo was involved. Pulse, blood pressure, respiration and galvanic skin response were measured steadily. Some psychological tests were provided to maintain the "experimental character" of the situation. The experimental subjects were observed during the experiment to detect any changes and they wrote a retrospective report on the experiment. This report was systematically analyzed for the appearance of psychological and psychophysical symptoms. Büttner concluded that the LSD responses were quite different from those of the placebo group (physical measures as well as psychological symptoms). However, she concluded that a broad variation was found in the responses and that every case had to be treated separately. This study is not comparable to an ideal hypothetical one which would use very low doses of LSD, leading to far fewer detectable symptoms. Moreover, one would expect stronger placebo reactions when a person exposes herself to the risk of being convicted for using an illegal drug.

Who would be willing to take such a risk, unless they expect a reward which outweighs the potential penalty?

In an early controlled experiment, Abramson et al. (1955e) were quite astonished at how many subjects had strong placebo reactions. One subject reacted positively to more than half of the items (of the LSD symptom questionnaire) over a 10-hour period. Another subject "had such a severe response to the placebo that considerable care was required to maintain an experimental situation that was not traumatic" (Abramson 1955e: 8). It appeared obvious to the authors that previous studies reporting on the effects of LSD-25 upon normal subjects needed re-evaluation in terms of placebo reactions. "… It was found by us that for a given group of individuals suitable evaluation of responses to LSD-25 could not be made without the use of a zero-dose control group". According to the authors, there were no studies in the literature at the time "which justify the conclusion that the symptoms reported, especially at low dosage, are significantly related to LSD-25 intoxication" (Abramson et al. 1955e: 8).

With this in mind, Abramson et al. (1955f) conducted an experiment for evaluating placebo responses in LSD research. Subjects expected to get an effective dose of LSD (and no placebo), which would produce a mild or a severe "psychotic reaction". The response was measured by the Cold Spring Harbor questionnaire of Abramson et al. (1955e). Thirty-three healthy subjects (age range 22–39 years) of average intelligence participated. Strong verbal and other suggestions were made to indicate that LSD would be given, which caused a large number of subjects to show a significant reaction to the questionnaire, sometimes in the range of the "real drug effects" (Table 15). However, whilst this experiment was blinded for the subjects, the researchers knew that no one would receive LSD. This fact might have reduced, but most probably not enhanced the placebo response. One implication of this experiment is that the "auto-suggestion" of the subjects was a major factor in their response. Abramson et al. concluded: "These observations emphasize once more the need for placebo controls in studies investigating the effects of drugs; without them changes which are produced merely by the situation and not by the drug are frequently falsely attributed to the action of the drug" (Abramson 1955e: 379).

On the other hand, there is a certain reliability in the responses of different subjects. The high correlations of responses of the same subjects under zero and under low and high doses of LSD-25 "… indicates a fairly high degree of predictability of the number of responses to the drug on the basis of the number of responses under the placebo" (Abramson et al. 1955e).

Are your palms moist?	60%	Do you feel unsteady?	25%
Does your head ache?	50%	Are you hot?	25%
Do you feel fatigued?	50%	Do your hands feel heavy?	25%
Do you feel drowsy?	50%	Do you feel weak?	25%
Are you anxious?	37%	Is salivation increased?	23%
Do you feel ill in any way?	28%	Do your hands and feet feel peculiar?	23%
Do you feel dizzy?	28%	Is your appetite decreased?	20%
Do you feel as if in a dream?	25%	Is there pressure in your ears?	20%
Is your appetite increased?	25%	Is your eyesight blurred?	20%

Table 15: List of symptoms and percentage of positive answers of thirty-three subjects who have been given a placebo, but told that they'd received LSD (Abramson et al. 1955e).

From the few facts and studies mentioned above it can be concluded that the so-called placebo response is an important part of the reaction to a drug, especially if its effects cannot be easily detected as is the case with low doses or microdoses of LSD. Expectation and (auto)suggestion will always play a more or less substantial role. According to scientific knowledge, it may lead to increases as well as decreases in performance.

	35–86B					20–58B					12–64A				
	in hours					in hours					in hours				
Question	½	1½	2½	3½	3½+	½	1½	2½	3½	3½+	½	1½	2½	3½	3½+
Are you nauseated?														X	
Is salivation increased?											X	X	X	X	
Do you have a funny taste in your mouth?						X	X				X			X	
Does your head ache?	X	X	X								X	X	X	X	
Do you feel dizzy?	X						X	X							

(continued...)

Question	½	1½	2½	3½	3½+	½	1½	2½	3½	3½+	½	1½	2½	3½	3½+
Are you sweating?															
Are you hot?								X	X						
Or cold?	X	X	X												
Are your palms moist?					X		X				X				
Is there pressure in your ears?	X	X	X								X	X		X	
Is your hearing abnormal?											X	X		X	
Is your eyesight blurred?	X	X	X			X									
Do you have difficulties in focusing your vision?															
Are the shapes and colours altered in any way?				X								X			
Do you tremble inside?											X	X		X	
Do you feel drowsy?								X	X						
Do you feel as if in a dream?	X					X	X	X	X						
Are you anxious?	X	X	X	X	X		X				X	X	X	X	

Table 16: Number of positive responses to some of Abramson's 47-item Cold Spring Harbor questionnaire for LSD symptoms in three subjects to whom placebo was administered (Abramson et al. 1955d)

Table 16 shows the positive responses of three out of five subjects who received placebo in a double-blind LSD experiment. The two other subjects did not generate any positive responses. They were called "placebo negative" by Abramson. The table demonstrates impressively how much placebo effects might be involved in any LSD experiment, especially if low doses are used, where subjects cannot easily detect psychological effects. This is one reason why microdosing especially is likely to be very vulnerable to placebo responses. Strictly controlled scientific experiments have to be conducted to find out more about the "real" effects of microdosing. Experienced LSD psychotherapist Betty Eisner comments, "we have seen reactions in a patient who has had no drug, and who has never had LSD or mescaline previously, which cannot be differentiated from reactions arising from 25 µg of LSD" (Eisner 1960: 45).

Researchers have given some suggestions as to how to distinguish reactions to LSD from those of placebo. For example, it was found that the peak of the drug reaction (with lower doses like 25–50 µg) is at the 1.5–2.5-hour point, whereas placebo responses typically peak 0.5–1 hours after ingestion (Abramson et al. 1955d). Sidney Malitz, a clinical LSD researcher with a lot of experience, found that neither visual effects (such as geometric forms of various colours and shapes), nor synaesthesia, have been induced by placebos. Therefore, he "feels that these phenomena are fairly specific for the hallucinogen group. I have seen all kinds of emotional reactions, such as euphoria, suspicion, depression, anxiety, and rage, occurring with placebos …" (Malitz 1960: 53). However, the fact that with low doses of LSD usually no visual effects occur, makes this a criterion of limited value.

Another problem is encountered when it comes to placebo reactions in experiments with LSD-like substances. This is the problem of different individuals reacting differently to the same dose of the same drug. This variability is known for many drugs, although not from e.g. an organism's reaction to the antibiotic effective for a certain disease. It appears obvious from numerous clinical experiments in humans that there are people who are very sensitive to LSD, and others who seem to be relatively insensitive to its effects. This complicates the design and results of experiments with LSD. As if this were not enough, there is also a possible difference in respect to the psychological level. One person might be very much in control of the effects of LSD, while another might not. This is dependent on the defence mechanisms of the subject and can also change once a person is very experienced with

LSD's effects. Hoffer has described such a subject (administered 100 µg), in whom he was unable to detect any LSD effect as an outside observer: "The subject was a psychiatrist who has probably taken it a hundred times. He has very excellent control. ... [W]ith all the ordinary clinical tests, no change is seen in judgement, in perception, or in mood" (Hoffer 1960: 41).

Another possible influence in respect to placebo effects could be a "forced placebo effect" (Passie 2002), which can be induced by a sub-perceptual impact of a drug, i.e. a drug effect registered by the physiology of the organism, but not perceived by the subject. In this situation, the organism might register a change, which could be unconsciously interpreted as a drug effect. This may become a "crystallization point" for an alteration of attention and may serve as a force to enhance the placebo response. This "forced placebo effect" could also play a role when an active drug is producing side effects, which are taken by the subject as a suggestion that the medication is working in the right way to produce the desired effects.

Medicinal chemist and prominent LSD scientist David Nichols appears to be sceptical about subjective responses to very low doses of LSD and the effects claimed for them. "If people have been told that taking one-tenth of a dose of LSD will enhance their creativity, some percentage of those taking that dosage will say they were more creative. [But] if psychoactive doses of LSD [100–200 µg] were to improve creativity, why would we expect that a much smaller dose … would have a similar benefit?" (Nichols 2017). One could argue that even a minimal "irritation" or "agitation" of the cognitive system can provide more space for new thoughts and ideas. However, if the effects are sub-perceptual (as with one definition of microdosing) this becomes much less likely.

11

Possible Mechanisms of Action

It is obvious from clinical and neuropsychological studies, which have been presented in the preceding chapters, that low doses of LSD (25–50 µg) can have significant effects on psychological functioning and some neurocognitive functions. Not much is known of the neurophysiological effects of these low doses, because no studies have been done on this aspect, certainly none using neuroimaging techniques. However, clinical and neuropsychological studies show that a lot of functions are influenced significantly by such small doses, suggesting that there are actions which impact upon brain functioning.

In respect to low-dose microdosing (5–20 µg) we have little evidence from clinical or neuropsychological studies of any kind of effects, not to mention neurophysiological effects. Only Greiner et al. (1958) showed that the human organism registers the action of very low doses of LSD by changes in pupil size and galvanic skin response.

It should be mentioned in advance that the issues of changes in pharmacokinetics from the use of low doses are significant, e.g. LSD has a much shorter duration of action with low doses (3–5 hours, compared to 8–12 hours with a dose of 100–200 µg, Diagram 2) (Stoll 1947, Dolder et al. 2017). It is also important to realize we know that at non-microdose amounts, a regular—e.g. daily—intake of LSD leads very quickly to a tolerance to the drug. This might interfere with dosing strategies amongst those who intend to take it on a daily or nearly daily basis. However, as of now we do not know exactly what the implications of these factors are at microdose amounts.

Because of the above-mentioned reasons, most of the following information is mainly provided to stimulate thoughts about possible mechanisms of action.

The serotonin neurotransmitter system

The major target of LSD's action is the serotonin neurotransmitter system. Therefore, some general properties of this system will be discussed. Serotonin or 5-hydroxytryptamine (5-HT) is one of the diverse neurotransmitters of the brain, and controls the activity patterns of many neuronal cells. The 5-HT system consists of several different receptor types, i.e. receptor subtypes. In the following paragraphs, their evaluation is limited to the two receptor subtypes mainly involved in the action of psychedelic drugs, but some general information on the 5-HT system will be provided.

It can be said in broad terms, that the brain's 5-HT system functions as a "modulator" to fine-tune the effects of the other neurotransmitter systems and their influence on behaviour. Because there seems to be no specific action for which the 5-HT system is responsible, it is said that the 5-HT system is "involved everywhere, but responsible for nothing".

If 5-HT is reduced in the brain (e.g. by dietary restrictions), impulsive and aggressive behaviours are increased. It has also been demonstrated that anxiety and stress increase synaptic 5-HT. It also seems that the 5-HT system serves to suppress behavioural responses to pain, anxiety, and aversive stimuli. Because of this, some authors have suggested that the brain's 5-HT system functions to alleviate psychological distress.

There is a lot of experimental evidence that 5-HT is involved in the regulation of mood, although exactly how is still virtually unknown. It is thought that the acute activation of 5-HT2A receptors by psychedelics does activate emotions, but does not modulate mood specifically, i.e. in a positive or negative direction. Antidepressants like Prozac® (fluoxetine) also indirectly target serotonin receptors, so it appears at least possible that a low, regular (e.g. one every few days) dose of a psychedelic might work in a somewhat similar fashion.

Serotonin receptors and psychedelics

The receptor subtype that is mainly involved in the action of psychedelics is the serotonin 2A (5-HT2A) receptor. Its basic function when activated is to increase the excitability of the host neuron. If the host neuron is excitatory (e.g. a pyramidal neuron), the outcome of its stimulation may be to increase its firing rate and the firing of those cells that it projects to. If the host cell is inhibitory, 5-HT2A stimulation will increase its firing and so enhance its inhibitory influence onto the neurons to which it projects. (Andrade 2011). The stimulation of the 5-HT2A receptor also leads to increased release of glutamate, a neurotransmitter that excites brain cells.

With respect to the receptor itself, Wacker (2017) has shown that the loop connecting the top of helix 4 to helix 5 (EL2) of 5-HT2B receptor folds over LSD after it binds in the receptor. EL2 forms a sort of "lid" over the LSD molecule after it binds to the receptor and "traps" LSD within the receptor for many hours. Being "trapped" in this way, LSD needs a considerable time to dissociate from the receptor, which might explain its long duration of action. The structure of EL2 in the 5-HT2A receptor is very similar to that of EL2 in the 5-HT2B receptor. Receptor kinetics studies presented in Wacker (2017) illustrate the very slow dissociation kinetics of LSD, in both the 5-HT2B and the 5-HT2A receptors.

When the population of 5-HT2A receptors is activated by moderate or medium doses of psychedelics (e.g. 100–200 μg LSD), it leads to a dramatic alteration of brain functioning and severe alterations of subjective experience and behaviour. With a dose of 100 μg LSD given by mouth, the maximum plasma concentration (Cmax) of 1.3 ng/ml has been measured. (Dolder et al. 2017). The affinity of a molecule to a receptor is usually measured in nanomol (nM). The affinity of LSD for the 5-HT2A receptor varies (depending on the study) between 0.5–10 nM. At a conservative estimate, it could be assumed that LSD's affinity for the 5-HT2A receptor is around 1 nM. Thus, with an LSD dose of 100 μg and the Cmax indicated by the above-cited study by Dolder et al. (2017), high enough brain concentrations can be expected to allow for a half-maximal occupation of 5-HT2A receptors in the brain, and presumably associated functional consequences. The magnitude of the functional consequences has not been seriously measured. However, drug concentrations in blood plasma and at the synaptic cleft do not always behave in a linear fashion, e.g. reaching the same range of concentration at both locations (in the same time span). Considering this, and given that pharmacokinetic and pharmacodynamics data on microdosing have so far not been established, any consideration about receptor occupation after sub-hallucinogenic doses can only be speculative.

Recent studies have shown that both the 5-HT2A and the 5-HT2B receptors recruit beta-arrestin2, a molecule that is part of a so-called second messenger system, i.e. a system that is induced by the activation of the receptor and leads to a cascade of further actions inside the cell. These second and third messenger systems are the ones that produce alterations in the functioning of the cells in question. That arrestin signalling is significantly involved in the action of LSD was recently proven in a genetically modified type of mouse, in which the gene that produces arrestin has been deleted. These animals did not show any typical responses after being given LSD. It is not known whether the rodent behavioural responses after LSD parallel particular psychological effects in man, so the importance of arrestin signalling to the overall effect of LSD in humans is unknown.

It was proposed that with moderate to higher doses of psychedelics the neurophysiological changes open a "window of plasticity" through the alteration of brain networks and their interplay, during which environment-related sensitivity is enhanced and significant therapeutic work can be done (Carhart-Harris & Nutt 2017).

Connectivity changes in brain functioning

It appears that the 5-HT system is very much involved in cognitive and psychological flexibility. Obviously, for every inner or outer life situation there is an optimal level of flexibility. One can envisage higher doses of psychedelics overshooting this through extreme 5-HT2A receptor activation, when an excessive flexibility might be caused that is not conducive to conventional cognition and behaviour, but which might lead to acute and long-term changes in experience and behaviour. Parts of these long-term changes in brain functioning can be understood in terms of connectivity, i.e. how the parts of the brain interact with each other to fulfil certain issues or activities. For example, the brain network that is active when we "do nothing in the outside world", the so-called Default Mode Network (DMN). LSD decreases functional connectivity within visual, sensorimotor and auditory networks and the DMN, while between-network connectivity is increased (all investigated networks were affected). Specific analyses indicated increased connectivity between networks and subcortical (thalamus, striatum) and cortical (precuneus, anterior cingulate cortex) hub structures (Carhart-Harris et al. 2016a, Mueller et al. 2018).

Studies have suggested that depression is linked to an overactive and somewhat "strengthened" DMN. It is possible that this causes excessive rumination, as well as frequently stepping out of the present moment to constantly question the past and the future. It was shown recently that the severe "irritation" of this kind of pathological brain activity in depressed patients by higher doses of psychedelic drugs like psilocybin or LSD can lead to significant betterment (Carhart-Harris et al. 2016).

The serotonin system and microdosing

David Nutt, professor of psychopharmacology at Imperial College London, who was involved with the recent neuroimaging studies with psychedelics, thinks that the psychedelic drugs "change cortical functions, making them more fluid and less rigid. At least big doses do ... and maybe low doses to a lesser extent. This may help certain brain areas work in more flexible and expansive ways ..." (Nutt, quoted in Bewellbuzz 2016). The hypothetical idea of "hyper-metabolism in the cerebral cortex" which may lead to "more information flow throughout the brain" points in a similar direction (Maloof, quoted in Cruz 2016: 44).

It is clear that despite all the older studies which have looked into the effects of low doses or microdoses of LSD, we have gained no significant knowledge with respect to their neurophysiological action. Therefore, in contrast to the effects of higher doses of psychedelics, virtually nothing is known about the neurophysiological effects of much lower doses or microdoses of psychedelics.

Some hypotheses about the therapeutic mechanisms of classical psychedelics like LSD or psilocybin have been described by Vollenweider and Kometer (2010). The stimulation of postsynaptic 5-HT2A receptors on a subpopulation of pyramidal cells in the deep layers of the prefrontal cortex by psilocybin or LSD leads to an increase in glutamatergic recurrent network activity and increased glutamatergic synaptic activity. Current models of emotion regulation suggest that the prefrontal cortex, including the anterior cingulate cortex (ACC) exerts 'cognitive', top-down control over emotion and stress responses through its connections to 'subcortical' brain structures such as the amygdala and the dorsal raphe. Reduced prefrontal glutamate levels are associated with attenuated PFC activation in response to emotional stimuli and have been reported in depressed patients. Depressed individuals and subjects with high trait anxiety might suffer from decreased top-down inhibition of amygdala activity. Normalization of this dysregulated network might be important in the recovery from depression. The chronic administration of LSD downregulates cortical 5-HT2A but not 5-HT1A receptors; this is most pronounced in the frontomedial cortex and the ACC. It is possible that such adaptations might underlie some therapeutic effects of hallucinogens in depression, anxiety and chronic pain.

Alterations of neuroplasticity?

Serotonin (5-HT) is known to play a vital role in brain development and plays a significant role in neural and behavioural plasticity into adulthood (Alboni et al. 2017). Neuroplasticity is the brain's ability to alter its neuronal connectivity patterns by losing some of the old neuronal connections and establishing new ones. There is evidence from animal studies that activation of the 5-HT system, especially the 5-HT2A receptor, may enhance neuroplasticity. As recent studies have shown, stimulation of the 5-HT2A receptor leads to an increased production of the Brain Derived Neurotrophic Factor (BDNF), which is taken as an indicator of neuroplastic changes. Animal studies have shown enhanced neuroplasticity even long after the effect of some drugs, not necessarily psychedelic drugs, has worn off. However, increases in BDNF are viewed by some scientists as a rather unspecific change that can be induced by several different conditions. We also don't know *how much* of a psychedelic substance is needed to increase neuroplasticity. Animal studies are usually conducted with very high doses of LSD and for longer time periods. It is also true that we don't know if possible neuroplastic changes lead to benign or dysfunctional changes of brain activity.

Do low doses act as a stimulant?

Most classic psychedelics like LSD have stimulant effects in the brain via the activation of 5-HT2A receptors, which increases the production of dopamine. Therefore, it is "... theoretically possible that low doses of LSD could enhance the biosynthesis of dopamine", states professor of pharmacology Dr David Nichols (Nichols 2017). It is at least theoretically possible that such an alteration could result in a mild stimulation, reminiscent of low doses of methylphenidate (Ritalin®) or modafinil (Provigil®). This explanation is appealing as people who microdose frequently report a coffee-like stimulation and claim to need less effort to maintain focus. A much stronger version of this effect is seen with classical stimulants as amphetamine or cocaine.

Might LSD work as a nootropic?

It is an eternal wish of humankind to live longer in a physically and mentally active and healthy state. From a pharmacological perspective, the industry has tried for quite a while to develop substances which can help the brain to stay mentally fit for a longer period of life. These drugs are called nootropics. It can be said that there have been no "breakthrough" drugs so far developed for this desirable effect. One of the more significant ones was the ergot derivative dihydroergotoxine mesylate (Hydergin®), which has some similarity in its molecular structure to LSD. Hydergin was first synthesized by Albert Hofmann. Studies have shown that Hydergin is able to enhance the brain's blood flow, if the blood flow is decreased by arteriosclerosis as in older people. It does not alter blood flow in people with normal blood flow (e.g. Mongeau 1974). Hydergin is still available in Europe for use in these patients.

Amanda Feilding, a British aristocrat involved with LSD research, believed the hypothesis that the main effects of LSD were caused by enhanced blood flow in the brain. However, Sokoloff et al. (1957) have shown that overall circulation of brain blood flow is not altered by LSD. More recently it was demonstrated that LSD alters blood flow in some regions of the brain which function as central hubs of the brain's connectivity networks (Carhart-Harris et al. 2012). However, these studies have been criticized because of a direct influence of LSD on the vessels, which might compromise results.

My personal thoughts about a possible nootropic effect of LSD go back to the mid-1990s. They were inspired by the fact that very few persons were known at that time who had taken medium range doses of LSD on a regular basis for more than 50 years. Two of those were Albert Hofmann (1906–2008) and his close associate, German writer Ernst Jünger (1895–1998). Both died when more than 102 years old and had very good mental performance until their death. My hypothesis is that if man goes through a usual life cycle, he collects a lot of tensions in his everyday life, which may pile up so much that he may end up with chronic tensions resulting in psychosomatic diseases. This process could hypothetically be counteracted by "regularly shaking the brain thoroughly around" through the activation of the serotonin system by LSD. In this way, as known from the catharsis-exerting effects of LSD in psychotherapy, one may get rid of those accumulated tensions—and stay psychologically and physiologically healthy for long. As it looks now, the new imaging studies with LSD point in this direction of a substantial "irritation" of the brain's networks through LSD, which ends up with a dissolution of the brain's encrusted networks' activity and a kind of "reset" of a constricted and dysfunctional pattern of brain activity (cf. Carhart-Harris & Nutt 2017).

In sum, the scientific results with respect to blood flow changes (as measured by fMRI) under psilocybin and LSD have to be replicated (preferably with other methods) before definitive conclusions can be made. Because ergot derivatives other than LSD—like Hydergin—might have different effects on the brain, they cannot be taken as evidence for effects of LSD. The efficacy of LSD as a nootropic, whether in a direct or indirect fashion, remains an open question.

Low doses of LSD and "psycho-integrative processes"

Harold Abramson theorized about the effects of low doses of LSD (20–40 μg) on human psychological functioning and possible psycho-catalytic or psychotherapeutic effects. He thought that low doses of LSD reduce the defensive mechanisms and that during the LSD reaction, the patient is able to bring up and integrate much material and insights, which were previously unavailable to conscious perception. Abramson called this alteration of defence mechanisms "ego-depression". Ego-depression typically occurs with doses of 25–50 μg and is accompanied by another process going on simultaneously, which he called "ego-enhancement". The interaction of these two processes going on simultaneously enhances "the ability of the individual under small doses of LSD-25 to face preconscious or unconscious material and to integrate this material into the dynamic forces of the ego-structure is not part of a loss of ego, but rather that of a reinforced ego which functions more effectively under the drug ..." (Abramson 1955: 153). However, Abramson (1960: 44) pronounces the fact that, "... the forces of the ego enhancement are supported by the intense relationship to the therapist. The patient's reaction is to LSD plus the therapist, and not to the LSD alone".

Stolaroff (1994) points in the same kind of direction, but without the necessity of the presence of a therapist, concluding that most people avoid taking lower doses because they don't want to encounter "uncomfortable feelings". Stolaroff recommended the use of low doses of psychedelics to work through and integrate those feelings in order to become psychologically healthier. The German LSD psychotherapist Walter Frederking (1955) reported that some of his patients had to get rid of "general tensions and inhibitions" by taking very low doses of LSD (20–50 μg) on a daily basis for less than a week.

Alterations of sleep and dreams

Interestingly, the only hard evidence that neurophysiological processes can be altered by very low doses of LSD comes from sleep research.

During the 1960s, a serotonin-dependent biochemical chain reaction was discovered, which modified the synaptic transmission in cholinergic structures of the hippocampus, apparently influencing the brain's theta activity and dreaming. Experiments showed that increasing serotonin in the brain extended the length of dreaming periods during the night (Oswald 1965), while lower serotonin shortens dreamtime (Matsumoto & Jouvet 1964). The first experiments on the influence of LSD (open, n = 3, 25 μg) on human sleep showed increased restlessness and extended REM periods (Toyoda 1964). Muzio et al. (1966) administered LSD (single-blind, crossover, n = 12, 6–40 μg) either shortly before sleep or 1 hour after sleep had begun. On the LSD nights, an extension of the REM periods was detected. After an extended REM phase, the next phase was always shorter, but the absolute REM period was also extended. Torda (1968) took EEG activity data from two test persons during 10 consecutive nights. During three of those nights, LSD (2.5 μg/min., i.v.) or placebo were infused at different times after the beginning of the third REM phase. LSD decreased the latency of the next REM phase to 10–19 minute(placebo: 40–60 min) and increased fluctuation of theta waves.

In sum, it appears that even microdoses can alter sleep and especially dreaming in healthy individuals. This could lead to an "indirect effect" on the psychological condition of a person microdosing with LSD. It seems at least possible that if an individual's brain state is affected during a period when the person isn't conscious, it might still have an impact on the psychological state during the day—or even for some days—after.

Do the neurocognitive alterations point in the direction of better functioning?

If one looks at the results of the neuropsychological tests with low doses of LSD, it appears that there are functions that are more or less compromised under the influence of low doses of LSD (Table 17). Complex functions such as mathematical abilities and intelligence are especially compromised. Lienert (1959, 1964) has reported an "ontogenetic regression" of intellectual functions under LSD (1 μg/kg) to an earlier level of development, equivalent to a 12–14-year-old. However, conventional neurocognitive measures are based on performance in the usual state of consciousness. These tests are therefore only able to measure *deficiencies* when it comes to "other modes of thinking/performing" as induced by psychedelics.

Measure	Dose (μg)	Results	References	Remarks
Arithmetic				
Addition tasks	50	n.s.c.	Primac et al. 1957	Consistently lower scores with LSD, but not significant.
Simple arithmetic problems	50	significantly less	Jarvik et al. 1955c	Lower performance by more time needed
Psychomotor performance				
Pursuit Rotor Test	50	n.s.c.	Primac et al. 1957	
Pursuit Rotor Test	50	n.s.c.	Kornetsky & Humphries 1957	
Pursuit Rotor Test	50	significantly less	Abramson et al. 1955a	
Dunlop Steadiness Test	50	n.s.c.	Primac et al. 1957	
Speed of coyping words	50	n.s.c.		
Chess performance	35	slight loss of skill	Ketchum 2006	
Size estimation	25,40	n.s.c.	Liebert et al. 1958	Estimation of own body size disturbed
Sustained attention	50	n.s.c.	Primac et al. 1957	Consistently lower scores with LSD, but not significant
Visual discrimination	50	Ca. 30% less	Primac et al. 1957	
Tactile discrimination	50	n.s.c.	Primac et al. 1957	
Bender Gestalt test	50	n.s.c.	Abramson et al. 1955e	Consistently lower scores with LSD, but not significant

(continued...)

Attention and concentration				
Simple discrimination	50	n.s.c.	Jarvik et al. 1955a	
Complex discrimination	50	n.s.c.		
Recall and recognition				
Verbal	50	n.s.c.	Jarvik et al. 1955b	
Visual	50	significantly less		
Selective recall	50	n.s.c.	Levine et al. 1955b	
Psycho-visual performance (spatial relations)	50	n.s.c.	Abramson et al. 1955c	Consistently lower scores with LSD, but not significant
Reaction time				
Auditory and visual	50	n.s.c.	Abramson et al. 1955b Kornetsky & Humphries 1957	
Manual	50	n.s.c.		
Time to read words	50	significantly less	Abramson et al. 1955b	
Learning	50	Learning decreased	Jarvik et al. 1955c	
Intelligence measures	50	n.s.c.	Levine et al. 1955b	"Pre-drug level of intellectual functioning maintained"

Table 17: Influence of low doses of LSD on neurocognitive and psychomotor functions. (n.s.c. – no significant change)

In addition, one has to consider the finding of Abramson (1960), who found a better performance with some individuals under the influence of doses of LSD as high as 100 µg. However, these cases seem to be very rare and those individuals had very specific abilities and talents.

When it comes to "creative thinking" it might be functional to be somewhat "irritated" in the usual way of mental functioning, which may help to gain "new" or unconventional thoughts, ideas or mental processes. However, usual neuropsychological performance results suggest a decrease in performance. Therefore, scepticism seems to be called for in place with respect to the reports of "better performance" under low doses of LSD or microdosing. However, whilst microdosing might not irritate the brain as much as with higher doses and not lead to performance deficits, it is unclear if a betterment of performance could be achieved in a reliable way.

In sum, it might be true that the irritation of the mental or cognitive system by low doses can lead to unusual thoughts, enhancement of creativity or unconventional solutions. It is at least theoretically possible that a certain "mental irritation" can transport a person out of their usual, maybe encrusted or fixated thought patterns ("log jams"), a process which might sometimes lead to "creative" solutions (cf. Harman et al. 1966). On the other hand, it is indicated one should expect a decrease in usual cognitive performance. One has to be aware that failures are generally much less reported than successes. For example, the dream of the chemist Kekule, which inspired the discovery of the ring structure of benzene, is still reported today, but all the myriads of dreams which lead to nothing more than bizarre imagery and thoughts are left unreported.

Conclusions

Is it probable that 10 micrograms of LSD can enhance creativity, improve focus, or clarity of thinking? It seems at least theoretically possible that a low dose of LSD might do something to the brain, because it can activate a significant number of serotonin (and possibly other receptors), at lower concentrations than a medium dose of LSD like 100 µg. However, if one thinks about a dose-response curve, there is no logical reason to expect that such a minute dose in the range of 5–15 µg would enhance performance or creativity (as doses of 100–200 µg might), let alone cause effects with respect to enduring mental focus as measured with drugs like modafinil or methylphenidate, as sometimes claimed. Effects in the range of minidosing (25–50 µg) are mostly distracting and irritating and have been demonstrated as such by scientific studies, However, it has also been shown that doses in this range can increase "divergent thinking" (e.g. Prochazkova et al. 2018), which has been discussed as a marker of creativity.

12

Possible Adverse Effects

On the following pages a description of possible side effects or adverse effects of microdosing will be discussed. It begins with claims made on relevant internet entries, articles, or books. The quality of the evidence is unquestionably low and cannot be taken as scientifically verifiable. Nevertheless, it is worthwhile looking at these accounts of possible side effects in order to give the reader an idea about them.

Even if one looks at all the reports on the internet, which number in the hundreds, one does not find many reports about side effects from microdosing, especially regarding people who may have mental health issues. We do not know how many of the non-respondents of Fadiman's survey included people who tried to follow the protocol but did not send in reports because they had a "no effect" experience or felt disagreeable side effects (and did not continue).

In general, studies with LSD and psilocybin have demonstrated that these substances are physiologically very safe if taken only occasionally. However, it remains unknown what effects *frequent* microdosing has on the human organism. This is why Austin (2017) recommends "microdosing for no longer than a few months at a time". Ingesting LSD for a period of many weeks or even months represents a time over which some chronic effects of LSD intake may become apparent. Humans have, in the past, been given doses of LSD for up to many months on a daily basis without any obvious damage (Bender & Sankar 1968), but the methods for detection of changes in the organism's hormonal balance and homoeostasis were not very broad or sensitive at the time.

Possible acute physical side effects

These seem to depend on the dose taken. With low doses of 25–50 μg the following side effects are repeatedly reported in the literature:

- Need for extra sleep at the end of the day
- Feeling more drained than usual
- Uncomfortable stomach feeling, e.g. like an empty stomach
- Restlessness
- Increased sweating

Austin (2018: 52) has found in his surveys that muscle and gastric issues were regularly reported.

Liddel and Weil-Malherbe (1953) have demonstrated that the blood level of adrenaline is significantly increased by even tiny amounts of LSD, although this reaction occurs only for a few hours. This could explain the symptoms of sweating and anxiety reported by some subjects. There is no data on long-term effects of this adrenergic stimulation.

Possible psychological adverse effects

Fadiman has received some reports of negative reactions. Several people reported uncomfortable sweating on dosing days (but usually did not stop dosing). Two people reported increased anxiety. One person reported more migraines (Fadiman 2016: 57). Another person claimed increased light sensitivity (Madeline in Fadiman 2011: 205). Two others stopped microdosing because of extreme fatigue on days 2 and 3, which are the dose-free "transition day" and "normal day", according to the Fadiman protocol.

Some users reported irritability, mood swings and increased anxiety after starting microdosing (Fadiman protocol). Others mentioned that they were fine on dosing days, but felt anxious and depressed on non-dosing days to the extent that they quit the experiment (Sapiensoup 2017). Paul Austin states that "emotional turbulence or anxiety" are possible side effects. In his view this is largely due to the fact that LSD amplifies your current mood, rather than acting directly as a stimulant or numbing agent (Austin 2017). A microdoser from Germany reported that he had disagreeable reactions during "waiting periods", such as when stopping at a red traffic light. He felt built-up tensions, became impatient, and felt an urge for body movement (Matrixblogger 2017).

It is known from therapeutic applications of low doses (20–50 µg LSD) taken on a weekly basis (as was usual with psycholytic therapy in the 1960s) that a psychic labilization can result and the strength of the ego and its functions compromised. A certain sensitization, "psychological vulnerability" and "strange thoughts" were also reported. In the case of such reactions, the psycholytic therapists advised stopping the LSD sessions until a re-stabilization was reached (e.g. Leuner 1981). These effects could also compromise any positive effects of microdosing.

As mentioned in another chapter of this book, there is an influence of very low doses of LSD on sleep patterns, especially on the Rapid Eye Movement (REM) phases of sleep, when most dreaming occurs. We do not know whether the effects that result from influences on sleep and dreaming for longer periods are positive or negative. And because the few experiments in this respect have only been done (and just for few days), we do not know how far the human organism adapts to these effects of LSD. There is only one report in the scientific literature that has looked for changes in dream patterns during the course of a series of low-dose psycholytic therapy sessions. Unfortunately, this report is only available as an abstract which does not contain results (Gnirss 1966).

In a general statement, Fadiman argues that one should not take psychedelics daily for a period of months, and that if an individual does not feel as though their microdose is beneficial, they should stop. It should be noted that his instruction, whilst sensible, does increase the skew of the anecdotal data collected towards those who report positive results from following the protocol.

Insomnia

It has been repeatedly reported that some microdosers experienced an inability to fall asleep, technically called insomnia (Fadiman 2016, Korb 2018, Johnstad 2018). This is especially so when people microdose in the later part of the day. If this is true it implies a dose range with (indirect) perceptible LSD effects. As LSD is known to heighten arousal of the central nervous system, it is no wonder that a certain amount of LSD might keep people awake, even against their will. However, there is no scientific study that has evaluated this claim with lower doses.

Decrease in performance

There are no virtually no controlled studies on the effects of microdosing with doses lower than 20 μg. Only the study by Greiner et al. (1958) has investigated such a low dose range. In that study, no alterations in performance were found, but the instruments used might have been insufficient to detect such changes.

When it comes to doses of 20 *μg* and above, the usual scientific experiments found deficits in performance in arithmetic and other neuropsychological tasks such as attention, concentration, and abstract thinking among other neurocognitive measures. In general terms, the "higher" the necessary cognitive performance is (e.g. hearing one tone for pushing a button, versus hearing two different tones and a visual stimulus at the same time, or adding numbers versus solving a mathematical equation), the more measurable the decrease in performance. While some measures like complex arithmetic performance or complex attentional tasks are more sensitive to LSD than to others, like psychomotor performance, are much more stable. However, insight-related performance can be lower, because it usually needs the (simultaneous) use of more than one neurocognitive ability. Potentially, doses of LSD of 20 *μg* or above can lead to noticeable decreases in performance of daily routines, especially when it comes to more elaborate tasks such as car driving, handling machinery or complex (theoretical or practical) work issues.

In conclusion, it is generally not recommended to take doses of more than 15 *μg* if one is supposed to "perform as usual" (or better). Special care must be taken, if potentially life-threatening activities such as rock climbing or car driving are to be done. This might be a different matter when engaging with some forms of "creative" work, where the conventional matrix of intellectual abilities may not be as important.

Overdosing

As mentioned above, it is hard to get the dose right when you do not know exactly how much LSD a black-market preparation contains. Besides this problem, it is obvious that some people might take a higher dose (beyond 25 μg) in order to definitely "feel it". But if an LSD microdose is taken in the context of work, one might not function as well if the dose is just a bit too high. As users put it: "Getting the dose wrong, ... can make for a challenging day in the office" (Bewellbuzz 2016). With an "overdose" in relation to microdosing one might become psychologically irritated, more emotionally vulnerable, more sensitive to sensory (over)stimulation, have a tendency for withdrawal, and may not be able to interact with others as eloquently. It is also possible that with an overdose one might exacerbate an underlying manic or depressive condition.

Reactions to microdosing in people with mental health issues

Virtually nothing is known about the reactions of people with serious mental health issues to low-dose LSD or microdosing. Fadiman has discouraged a person with bipolar and sleep disorder from stopping microdosing (Fadiman quoted in Waldman 2017: 108/9), and he states that he received reports from "several people" who had been helped with their depression by this practice. Such claims can be found regularly on internet sites, as well as in Waldman's (2017) book. However, an early study by Savage (1952) has shown that there is no consistent response in depressives from daily low doses of LSD (20–80 µg). On the other hand, no complications with this daily dosing regimen were reported by Savage. One should remember that one's current mood is usually amplified by 25–200 μg doses of LSD, which may lead to a worsening of mood in depressed individuals. Nevertheless, it is premature to draw any serious conclusions about the Fadiman protocol, where 10–20 μg LSD are taken on the dosing day and there are two drug-free days in between the dosing days. These tiny doses are not expected to affect mood in an obvious way, but whether or not they might lead to subtle effects on basic mood over the course of weeks or months, as is reported by some users, is unknown.

If you are experiencing any mental health issues, and are interested in the possibility of microdosing, it is strongly recommended that you discuss the risks with your physician, especially if you have a diagnosis of psychosis, depression, or anxiety.

Possible long-term physical adverse effects

Some adverse consequences might result from a daily or every-few-days dosing regimen. Despite the vast spectrum of studies in the past, we do not know much about any potential long-term changes in the hardware of the human organism that may result from long-term regular LSD use. Professor

Nichols said this: "Using these drugs once a month is one thing. Using them every day, I'm not sure they are innocuous. They may bring about subtle behavioral and hormonal changes that we don't yet fully understand" (Nichols, quoted in Bewellbuzz 2016). If one accepts anecdotal evidence, one may point to the case of Amanda Feilding, who claims that she has taken thousands of doses of LSD since the 1960s, sometimes for periods of months on a daily basis. To all appearances, she is quite lucid today after all these experiments.

Possible tissue alterations

There is a potential risk of tissue alterations with taking psychedelics like LSD over a long period of time—although we do not know how this translates to microdosing.

The first indication that medically used drugs derived from the ergot fungus could be responsible for an inflammatory process of fibrosis (in the retroperitoneum, the heart and the lungs) came from a case series of Graham (1967). He found fibrotic tissue alterations resulting from prophylactic long-term treatment of migraine with methysergide, a derivative of lysergic acid (as is LSD). Retroperitoneal fibrosis is a rare condition in which the ureters and other retroperitoneal structures become encased in a mass of dense fibrous tissue (Andersohn & Garbe 2009). No dose- or time-dependence is known for this effect, i.e. there is no linear relation to the dose and length of administration of the drug. This tissue alteration is not limited to retroperitoneal tissue; it can also induce changes in the heart-valve tissue, which can lead to valvular dysfunction. Withdrawal of the drug is followed by partial or complete regression of the tissue alteration (Roth 2007).

As LSD is a derivative of ergot somewhat similar to methysergide, it could potentially also lead to tissue alterations if taken on a regular basis. It is known that these tissue alterations are caused by the activation of the 5-HT2B receptor (which is indeed potently activated by LSD). 5-HT2B receptors regulate serotonin release and serotonin levels in blood plasma via the serotonin transporter (Nebigil et al. 2001). Long-term activation of this receptor stimulates growth of cardiac ventricular and valve tissue. An example for this is the anorectic drug fenfluramine, which stimulates the 5-HT2B receptor and has been taken daily for months. It has caused Valvular Heart Disease (VHD) and was withdrawn from the market. A possible risk in this respect by taking LSD on a regular basis cannot be excluded. To quote LSD expert Professor David Nichols again, "some may trivialize this concern, in the belief that microdoses are too low to cause VHD. A 2017 study ... of LSD binding to the 5-HT2B receptor shows that it is 'trapped' within the receptor for many hours ... Thus, even low doses could be problematic" (Nichols 2017).

However, up to now no cases of VHD have been described for users of LSD. Adults have been given medium doses of LSD for up to 77 days in medically supervised settings without any observable damage (Isbell et al. 1956), although at that time no echocardiograms were recorded to examine cardiac structure. However, the researchers were MDs and would have detected grave distortions of cardiac functioning, which would have happened if fibrosis had been induced to a significant degree. Children have been treated for autism and schizophrenia with daily doses of 100–250 µg given for months (up to 35 months in some cases) without any detectable damage (Bender & Sankar 1968), but again without examination of cardiac tissue. One should bear in mind however, that the examinations and instruments used at that time might not have been sensitive enough to detect damage.

Possible effects on chromosomes, fetus and cancerogenicity

One scientific study in 1965 suggested that LSD in very high doses causes chromosomal changes in animals. Additional studies, however, failed to replicate that result. Nevertheless, the reputation of LSD being a non-toxic and physiologically well-tolerated compound was seriously damaged by these findings. Later research has concluded that this "chromosomal damage" was irrelevant and did not imply malformation of offspring or infertility. However, it is not certain that a daily or nearly daily intake of LSD will not alter the human organism with respect to chromosomes, mutagenic, teratogenic, or carcinogenic effects. The studies done, especially those in humans (under controlled conditions with pure LSD) are limited to a small number of exposures. Users of illicit LSD consistently showed worse results, but this may have to be attributed to the general problem of illicit drug abuse, and the lifestyle usually associated with it. As we do not know much, the few scientific ideas and findings that are relevant will be presented here.

In 1980, the prominent LSD therapist Stanislav Grof reviewed all the scientific, experimental and other evidence about possible chromosomal and other toxicological long-term damage, as shown in animal and human experiments. Here are his conclusions about this complex experimental matter.

> *Two-thirds of the existing in vitro studies [= experiments on tissues and cells, not living organisms] have reported some degree of increased chromosomal breakage following exposure to illicit and pure LSD. With one exception, these changes were observed with concentrations of LSD and durations of exposure that far exceeded the dosages commonly used in humans. In none of the studies was there a clear dose-response relationship. Since similar findings have been reported with many commonly used substances, including artificial sweeteners, aspirin, caffeine, phenothiazine tranquilizers and antibiotics, there is no reason why LSD should be singled out and put in a special category. There is no justification to referring to the structural changes of the chromosomes as 'chromosomal damage'; their functional relevance and relation to heredity remains to be established. ... In some early studies, LSD was implicated as a potential cause of congenital malformations [= birth defects], abortions and fetal wastage. The original reports of teratogenic effects in hamsters, rats and mice have not been confirmed by later studies. The experiments in rodents indicated a rather wide range of individual strain and species susceptibility to the effects of LSD. It is highly questionable whether and to what extent the results of such investigations can be extrapolated to humans. ... There is no clear evidence that pure LSD is teratogenic in humans. ... There is no clinical or experimental data demonstrating that LSD has carcinogenic [= cancer inducing] properties, as suggested by some of the earlier studies. No increase in the incidence of tumors among LSD users has ever been detected.*
> (Grof 1980: 340/341)

With respect to the chromosome issue, it has to be added that the aberrations measured (whatever their hereditary significance) do return to normal limits in a few weeks in mice (Cohen & Mukherjee 1968) and humans (Tijo et al. 1969). However, most of the experiments and clinical observations to which Grof is referring were done under conditions of only a few exposures to LSD, not when given on a long-term or daily basis. Therefore, some potential risks might not have been detected.

Possible impact on neurotransmitters

Most studies in the past did not use any parameters (endocrine or other) which could inform us about long-term changes in the "hardware" of the human organism. As far as we know, the organism has a mechanism to cope with the effect of chronic administration of a substance like LSD through the development of tolerance.

It also appears possible that even very low doses can interact with the rate of production and metabolism of the neurotransmitter serotonin and with the secretion of dopamine (cf. Nichols 2017). We cannot know from the available data if and to what extent any long-term effect might result in this respect. On the other hand, as neuroscientist David Presti has stated: "Whatever risk there is, is likely to be less than those associated with antidepressant medication use for extended periods of time" (Presti quoted in Waldman 2017: 108). And there is evidence that long-term use of SSRIs depletes serotonin and alters its production.

During the last 40 years of research on LSD and related substances, we have not paid much attention to the rate of turnover of the brain's serotonin. In the 1950s and 1960s, methods available for studying neurotransmitters were rather rudimentary, but it was possible to study serotonin turnover in rat brains.

To explore possible persistent metabolic effects in chronic LSD users, Diaz and Huttunen (1971) gave LSD orally at doses of 20 µg/kg per day to rats for one month. Eighteen hours after the final dose, a 25--30% increase in the synthesis and turnover of serotonin was noted. The whole brain concentrations of the serotonin precursor tryptophan (18%) and serotonin itself (13%) were also increased. The authors of this study claimed that their dose was comparable to those typically used by humans, but this is not an established fact because these kinds of scaling from animal to humans is known to be unreliable. Therefore, it is unclear if the results of this study has relevant implications for humans.

In an experiment on rabbits, Sankar et al. (1961) gave the animals 0.92 mg of radioactively-labelled serotonin. The control animals were sacrificed after 60 minutes. Another group of animals received 500 µg LSD, 45 minutes after they had received the radioactive serotonin, and were sacrificed 15 minutes thereafter. Liver, lung, kidneys, spleen, heart, cerebrum, cerebellum, brain stem, and the rest of brain were assayed for total radioactivity and serotonin radioactivity. LSD increased serotonin by 30-50% in all tissues (except the cerebrum and the heart), but less so in visceral tissues.

Flashback phenomena and Hallucinogen Persisting Perceptual Disorder (HPPD)

There are no reports to date that mention phenomena like flashbacks or so-called Hallucinogen Persisting Perceptual Disorder (HPPD) to be associated with microdosing. Yet, the possibility of these phenomena occurring cannot be excluded and will therefore be described here. Flashbacks are after-effects of the ingestion of hallucinogens and certain other drugs. They are defined as the re-occurrence of perceptual or feeling changes that were first experienced under the influence of a drug. Usually these are harmless phenomena which last mere seconds and do not cause significant suffering (cf. Holland & Passie 2010, Halpern & Pope 2003). They usually disappear in the days or weeks after drug ingestion. Hallucinogen Persisting Perception Disorder (HPPD) is different from flashbacks and is claimed to be a continuous change in visual perception like "steadily seeing white snow" or "trails associated to movements of things". It appears somewhat astonishing that no case of HPPD was ever reported from all the experimentation up to the 1960s on more than 10,000 experimental subjects and patients. However, some authors believe that it is a real disease entity, even if all the "case series" or "case reports" are based on subjective statements. The only studies that tried to verify these phenomena had numerous flaws (Abraham and Duffy 1996, 2001). The first systematic study, which investigated 23 individuals who claimed to suffer from HPPD, found that virtually all had significant psychiatric comorbidity and most had experienced visual phenomena before they ingested hallucinogens (Halpern et al. 2018).

It is also worth noting that, even if there were a corroborated risk of developing flashbacks or HPPD with medium or higher doses of LSD, the risk may be absent or minimal with very low doses. For example, it is known that flashbacks appear more frequently after so-called "bad trips" or "horror trips", i.e. experiences which have a serious negative impact on the psychological state of the person.

Possible interactions with "antidepressant" drugs

The interactions between LSD and "antidepressants" are of interest in respect to the mechanism of action of hallucinogens. The early concept of LSD–serotonin antagonism was pursued by numerous researchers (cf. Aghajanian, 1994). After the previous decades had seen more precise characterization of the subtypes of 5-HT receptors, selective studies were undertaken, including some with anti-depressants. The concept of LSD–serotonin antagonism was pursued by numerous researchers. An association of depression with the serotonin system was suggested, although this was not supported with hard scientific evidence. Nevertheless, the major "antidepressant" drugs of today target the serotonin system. As mentioned in another chapter, the evidence for the efficacy of these drugs became questionable after data were re-analyzed recently (e.g. Kirsch et al. 2008, Moncrieff 2008).

Not much is known in the scientific literature about the interaction of LSD and "antidepressant" drugs. What is known will be presented here. Resnick et al. (1964) treated test subjects for a period of weeks with an MAO inhibitor (in animal studies, this treatment results in an elevation of serotonin in the brain). Four men were exposed to six experimental situations in which they received LSD (open, randomized, crossover, n = 4; 40 or 75 µg), either with or without isocarboxazid pretreatment (2- or 5-week intake of 30 mg/day). All the subjects reported LSD activity that was reduced or eliminated by pretreatment with the MAO inhibitor. The outcome measures were interviews, behavioural observations, psychological tests, and physiological studies. A 3-day pretreatment with the "antidepressant" drug tranylcypromine (70 mg/day), also an MAO inhibitor, led to a pronounced reduction of typical LSD symptoms (open, cross- over, n = 8; 100 µg), but without influencing mydriasis (Marecek et al. 1968). A single dose of isocarboxazid, given before LSD, has been demonstrated to have no influence on LSD effects in humans (DeMaar et al. 1960).

Grof and Dytrych (1965) investigated the interaction between "antidepressants" and LSD in 11 neurotic patients. Patients were first treated with 250–500 mg/day Niamid® i.v. (nialamide) and then 150–300 mg/day per os over a longer period of time (not specified). One day after discontinuing nialamide, various doses of LSD (150–500 µg) were given. Doses of up to 400 µg LSD caused only minimal or no effects. In later tests, the interval between the last dose of nialamide and the intake of LSD was lengthened. The finding was that up to 14 days after discontinuing the antidepressant a strong resistance to LSD remained. In an experiment with three neurotic patients, nialamide was given daily for 3 weeks up to an absolute dose of 3,500 mg. In this case, renewed administration of LSD resulted in no clinical symptoms.

Bonson et al. (1996) reported on 33 people (8 women, 25 men) aged 15–37, who were all treated for at least three weeks with an antidepressant (28 with an SSRI) before they took LSD in recreational settings. Of the 17 people who were given fluoxetine (Prozac), a significant reduction of effects of LSD was described in 88% of the cases. This reduction did not appear to depend on the dose of the SSRI. Sertraline (100–200 mg/day) was taken by nine subjects. With the exception of one person, all of them noticed a significant attenuation of the LSD action. One subject stopped taking sertraline 36 hours before LSD; a noticeable reduction in the effect was still observed. One month after discontinuation of fluoxetine, LSD effects were again felt as usual. The reduction of LSD effects could be due to an adaptation of the serotonergic system, including changes to 5-HT1A and 5-HT2A/5-HT2C receptors and the extracellular serotonin concentration, as well as changes in the catecholamine system. Increased extracellular serotonin could additionally have led to 5-HT2A receptor downregulation, thus decreasing the density of the receptors necessary for the action of LSD.

In a further observational study, Bonson and Murphy (1996) interviewed 10 people with previous LSD experience who had taken LSD with a tricyclic antidepressant (TCA), an MAO inhibitor, or lithium. The five people on a TCA reported a potentiation of the LSD effects. The two people treated with MAO inhibitors showed almost no LSD effects after taking LSD. Three subjects were treated with lithium alone or in combination with imipramine. They reported enhancement of all the effects of LSD.

CAVEAT: The combination of lithium (a medication used for prophylactic treatment of bipolar mood disorder) and LSD appears to carry a particularly high-risk potential. A temporary comatose state has been induced by an accidental co-ingestion of both substances. This threatening condition disappeared after the injection of diazepam without leaving any detectable damage (Middendorf 2001).

Interactions with cannabis

In animal experiments, daily doses of LSD (130 μg/kg, intraperitoneal (i.p.)) for three days did not influence effects of tetrahydrocannbinol (THC) (130 μg/kg, i.p.), the main ingredient of marijuana, nor vice versa (Silva et al. 1968). Isbell and Jasinski (1969) investigated cross-tolerance in 10 former opiate addicts who were given 0.5–1.5 μg/kg LSD on 11 consecutive days. On the twelfth day, the application of THC (250 μg/kg, per inhalation) was just as potent as it was prior to the LSD pretreatment.

Possible interactions with other medications

On their website on microdosing, Fadiman and Korb present a list of at least 185 different conventional medications that seem not to interfere with microdosing. Some may interpret this as evidence that "no effects" seen from microdosing interactions equals "no interaction with other medications". In this author's opinion, this is just anecdotal evidence and further studies are needed.

Possible contraindications

No definitive conclusions can be made about possible dangers and contraindications of microdosing, but Fadiman has concluded from his survey data that some people should not take microdoses for various reasons. In a preliminary statement, he suggested these situations in which microdosing might be not a good idea:

- Pregnancy
- Prior history of psychosis
- Individuals in terrible external circumstances
- Situations such as losing a pet or having sick pets
- Individuals whose only symptom was anxiety
- Long term progressive illness, such as multiple sclerosis (MS)

At a recent conference, Korb (2018) reported that persons with an autism spectrum disorder seem to need higher doses of LSD (and psychedelics in general) for the full response. This in turn suggests a microdose of 50 μg LSD in this population, which she does not want to recommend. Therefore, these patients should not microdose.

13

Some Psychophysical Issues

The issue of selective recall

It is well known from research on memory that there is selective recall of certain events, e.g. subjects selectively remember some features of a situation they have experienced, but miss some others. In scientifically designed experiments, Bartlett (1932) has shown that subjects who have been shown a film tend to change an unusual pattern in a film to a more conventional one, when asked to recall it a while later.

In respect to hallucinogens, a few studies were conducted in this direction. A very experienced researcher, Hollister (1968: 36), reported from his studies with LSD and related hallucinogens that:

> *a peculiar phenomenon observed in our studies was one of selective recall. When patients were asked to rate their feelings during the study, most reported changes which might be regarded as unfavorable; that is, they became less friendly, energetic or clear-thinking and more aggressive, jittery and depressed. Yet when asked to choose adjectives which best described the total experience several hours after it was completed, most often commendatory adjectives were chosen;*

illuminating, pleasurable, beneficial, satisfying and relaxing. ... Misperceptions, auditory hallucinations, and somatic or paranoid delusions were least often reported.

In a study about alterations in the recall of an LSD experience, subjects filled in a questionnaire again six months after the initial experience. It was demonstrated that those items related to anxiety and loss of control were scored much lower than when the questionnaire was taken immediately after the experience (Linton et al. 1964). Bodmer (1999) did a study which assessed the recall of an altered state of consciousness induced by hallucinogenic drugs. She evaluated answers to questionnaires given at different time points after the drug experience, and found that subjects had a significant tendency toward the positive or the negative pole, i.e. they tended to give the experience a certain direction and lose the ambiguity with the passage of time.

These studies show that there are significant issues with selective recall that have to be considered, especially with low doses, where the effects are definitely less impressive and memorable. Effects of this kind might also add to possible placebo effects.

Is there evidence for a carry-over effect during the days after a microdose?

From a strict pharmacological point of view it is not obvious that a small dose taken in the morning would have any effects the next day. The half-life of LSD is around 135 minutes, which implies that only half of the dose of the drug remains in the human organism approximatively 2.5 hours after entering it. During the next 135 minutes the remaining amount of substance will have halved. After an additional 135 minutes, another half of the substance has gone. Roughly speaking, after 7 half-life times (i.e. ca. 16 hours) nearly all of a low dose will be out of the system. These half-lives were calculated after administration of large doses of LSD, so microdoses may clear the body even more rapidly. Therefore, it can safely be said that after 24 hours a microdose of LSD has left the system completely (cf. Passie et al. 2008, Dolder et al. 2017). In addition, Liechti (2018) has estimated that the metabolism and elimination of low doses like 25–50 μg leads to an inactive plasma level of LSD in a much shorter time. If true, this would imply that the development of tolerance might be to a lesser degree, or even non-existent, with daily low doses of 10–25 μg.

However, there is a definite possibility that other kinds of carry-over effects can occur. When the serotonergic system in its usual configuration is perturbed by the effects of a drug, the induced changes might require some time until the organism has re-adapted to a homoeostatic state. In the case of LSD, it appears possible from some data presented here that an effect of very low doses of LSD on sleep and dreaming might influence physiological processes during the next day (cf. Muzio et al. 1966). We also know nothing about the effects of low doses of LSD on the production of potent hormones such as cortisol, or melatonin.

Can bad sleep enhance effects of microdosing?

I still have a vivid memory of the time when I was lucky to work with Professor Hanscarl Leuner (1921–1996), who was one of the leading European experts on the clinical use of hallucinogens. We treated patients with low doses of psychedelics in the "psycholytic" fashion (cf. Passie 1996/1997). Usually the patients were interviewed on the day of the session directly before the drug was given. The conversations centred around the biography and the actual state of the patient and his life, i.e. the "set". In addition, Leuner usually asked the patients how they had slept the night before. When they said "I slept well" he answered "oh, then the substance will not work as well". It was his suggestion that when a person has not slept well, he will have a more intense experience during the psycholytic session. Some time later, I found that there were two studies which had looked at this phenomenon. In a study by Bliss et al. (1959), healthy subjects initially received a low dose of LSD (n = 4, 0.5 μg/kg). On the next test day, the dose was doubled. In these two experiments, the subjects only perceived noticeable LSD effects with the higher dose. In the second part of the study, the subjects were not allowed to sleep for 48 hours and were then given 0.5 μg/kg LSD. The hallucinatory effects with this dose were described by them as more intense than at 1.0 μg/kg without the sleep deprivation. In another experiment, Safer (1970) gave test subjects LSD (single-blind, n = 33, 1.5 μg/kg) or placebo after one or two nights without sleep. Outside observers did not note any great differences, but psychometric testing was significantly worse for those who had received the LSD, showing more weaknesses in vigilance and accuracy of perception when sleep deprivation was added.

Can changes of pupil diameter be detected by outside observers?

There has been much discussion on Internet microdosing forums as to whether changes in pupil diameter are easily detectable by outside observers, which could put a person at risk of being recognized as being under the influence of a drug. It became clear in clinical LSD studies that there is no symptom or side effect caused by LSD that will always occur (e.g. Grof 1980). It was claimed early on that pupil diameter changes correlate strongly with psychological effects, and that if no pupil reaction is observed, no psychological reaction will occur (e.g. Sandison 1960). In fact, changes in pupil diameter were found to be the most consistent effect of LSD in humans. Greiner et al. (1958) have observed small pupil diameter changes with doses as low 5 *μg*. However, these were only detectable by special instruments, and were not ordinarily visible. Internet forums on microdosing have stated that the pupil response is somewhat dependent on the individual person's reaction. However, for most people pupil dilation should not be an issue with doses below 20 μg. Above 20 *μg* it might be noticeable in some persons, but in general up to 40 μg could be used without major pupil dilation. Apparently experienced authors writing on an Internet source about this "problem" concluded from their experience that:

> *pupil dilation is not something I would personally worry about when microdosing. For most people it won't happen, for some people their pupils might dilate slightly, and for a very small group of people it will be obvious. Try to test if your pupils dilate when microdosing, but remember that people in general are not very observant ...*
> (Anonymous 2017).

Specific research problems with microdosing and minidosing

It might be that anecdotal reports of microdosing point to a "real" effect which has not been detected up to now because no controlled experiments have been done to investigate it, or else the instruments have not been sensitive enough to detect it. The major problems with these anecdotal reports are interferences from placebo effects, spontaneous and circadian fluctuations in a person's performance, and spontaneous changes in conditions of mental conditions such as anxiety and depression or other "pathological" conditions. Another serious problem is that a "recreational user" often does not know what the substance they have acquired actually is, nor precisely how much of it they have actually taken. This makes any such uncontrolled experiment a crude endeavour in comparison to exact science. These problems can only be solved by a rigorous scientific study, which uses a double-blind placebo-controlled design, with careful objective and subjective measures.

Scientists are less than optimistic when it comes to getting approval in the US for a study on the present standard version of microdosing. From the authorities' point of view, such a study would imply dosing a subject with a Schedule I substance and sending them out into the world under its influence (if testing were to recreate the "going about one's normal daily tasks" remit of the standard microdose regimen), which might look like doing something illegal and under somewhat "uncontrolled" circumstances, including potential dangers. Other researchers disagree with this perspective by pointing to the fact that clinical research means that in a lot of cases patients on medications are sent out into everyday life, even when the substances used are known to compromise the subject's abilities to function. However, these substances are non-scheduled compounds in approved clinical tests. It is also worth reminding ourselves, physicians regularly send people home with a supply of dangerous drugs to self-administer (e.g. opioids) for their illnesses. However, the fact that as there is no "real benefit" to be obtained from microdosing, as there is no medical disorder to be cured, means it might be hard to find sponsors and get approval for such a study.

When it comes to studies in the past that have used low doses of LSD and sent subjects "out into real life", two examples can be given. Leuner, in association with Schönfelder, conducted a study in which healthy volunteers were administered low doses of CZ-74 (a short-acting psilocybin derivative), after which their performance was observed and signs of subtle psychopathology were looked for, possibly similar to those of "beginning schizophrenia" à la Conrad (1958). After administration of the drug, the subjects were sent home to go on with their usual everyday activity—and asked to watch for psychopathological signs. It was found that they experienced some significant psychopathology as typical for the syndrome of "beginning schizophrenia", but other than these subtle psychopathological changes no adverse reactions were registered from this experiment (Schönfelder 1967, Leuner & Schönfelder 1981).

In a similar kind of study, Vojtechovsky et al. (1972) dosed 12 healthy volunteers with 20 μg LSD in a double-blind design. Subjects were paired and received either LSD-placebo, LSD-LSD or placebo-placebo. Their social performance was observed in the laboratory and while performing social contacts in town (e.g. shopping, making travel arrangements). Interestingly, it was found that subjects could control their behaviour and psychological reaction better when they were outside the laboratory. No obvious dangers or performance deficits were reported during this experiment.

14

Low-Dose Psychedelics and Creativity

From the late 1960s onwards, one can see that psychedelic drugs have obviously inspired culture, most clearly in the fields of painting and music (e.g. Masters & Houston 1968, McDonough 1985, Canamo 2004, Durr 1970). However, only a few attempts have been made to scientifically study the possible influences of psychedelics on creativity. Krippner (1985) has given a good review of most of these studies. It appears appropriate here to mention some definitions, significant scientific studies, and to outline a few principles.

The inner conditions to foster creativity were formulated by creativity researcher Rogers (1959). Because nothing else has improved upon his work since that time, his definitions are given here:

- Low degree of psychological defensiveness; lack of rigidity and permeability of boundaries in concepts, beliefs, perceptions, and hypotheses; tolerance for ambiguity where it exists, ability to receive and integrate apparently conflicting information; sensitive awareness of feelings and openness to all phases of the experience.
- Evaluative judgements based primarily, not on outside standards or prejudices, but on one's own feelings, intuition, aesthetic sensibility, a sense of satisfaction in self-expression, etc.
- The ability to 'toy' with ideas, colours, shapes, hypotheses; to translate from one form to another; to think in terms of analogues and metaphors.

It is obvious that some of these requirements can be provided by (parts of) the psychedelic experience.

Alterations of consciousness resulting from psychedelics share characteristics with mental states associated with creativity, they often permit access to preverbal impressions, to unconscious material, and to the intuitive process. It should be noted that the transcendence of culturally imposed imprints and of societal conditioning has always been a goal for creative persons (Masters & Houston 1968; Krippner 1969: 290).

Scientific studies on psychedelics and creativity

The earliest trials under controlled conditions were conducted with mescaline by Maclay & Guttman (1941) and with LSD by Tonini and Montanari (1955) using artists as the experimental subjects. The artists were asked to paint under the acute effects of the drugs. As these authors followed the paradigm that these drugs induce "temporary psychotic states" it is no wonder they concluded that the artistic production "… reflect pathological manifestations of the type observed in schizophrenia" (Tonini & Montanari 1955: 238).

Arieti (1976: 371) has speculated that the enhanced imagery under psychedelic drugs can only be made use of when more complex mental activity, which is disturbed under LSD, is involved. Somewhat consistent with this, Berlin et al. (1955) found poorer technical execution with painting when graphic artists had been given LSD and mescaline. One of the subjects in Barron's (1963: 251) study on creativity with psilocybin commented: "I have seldom known such absolute identification with what I was doing—nor such a lack of concern with it afterward". In general, these early studies, including Janiger's study on painting of Kachina dolls under LSD (Dobkin de Rios & Janiger 2006), have shown that imagery and creativity can be enhanced in some artists, but the technical difficulties to transform the alterations of perceptions into elaborated works of art are significant. The same was found in a study on twenty prominent artists (e.g. Friedensreich Hundertwasser) at the German Max-Planck Institute for Psychiatry, who were given LSD in moderate doses (Hartmann 1974). Some of the artists were able to work under the influence of the drug, while others had positive as well as significant negative experiences, which interfered with their work. Nevertheless, somewhat "more creativity" while working under the influence of the drug (as well as afterwards) could be demonstrated in some of the artists. Hartmann's study suggests that the LSD experience was more of an inspiration than a repeatable brain state with better creative performance.

Fischer et al. (1972) administered a moderate dose of psilocybin to 21 college-age volunteers. A creativity measure was applied. There was no consistent "creative" response for the whole group, but intuitive subjects with a large perceptual-behavioural variability and a field independent cognitive style were found to have more creative experiences during the drug-induced state. However, only a few of them were able to transform these experiences into real creative work. The decrease in motor performance, concentration and selective attention likely contributed to this. The authors concluded that "the widely held generalization that hallucinogenic drugs impair performance cannot be maintained, since we have found that certain inter-individual differences may disappear under hallucinogenic drug-induced arousal, while others become manifest only under drug-influence" (Fischer et al. 1972: 35).

Results of these studies point to the complexity of the issue and indicate that creativity can be enhanced in some individuals, but not in others.

Mescaline and creativity

German psychologist Gisela Kreppel (1964) has researched "phenomena at the threshold level of mescaline" (her dissertation's title), which included a measure of creativity. The dose was 50–70 mg in the low-dose group and 140–200 mg in the high-dose group. Twenty-four healthy females and 26 males (age range 19–42 years) were tested. The creativity measure was the Sander Phantasy Test. The test consisted of five paper sheets. On each sheet, a fragment of a light pencil drawing is given (e.g. three wave-like lines) and the subjects asked to use it to draw something "out of it". Measured are speed, order of space, colours, and physiognomic qualities. Psychomotor speed was significantly decreased under mescaline. Drawing of space became disharmonious and technically inadequate. Subjects were unable to structure and use the room appropriately. With respect to colouring, the drugged persons used many more colours in comparison to their pre-experimental drawings. The physiognomic qualities of the drawings decreased significantly and they looked more confused, and fragmented.

A prominent study into the creative potential of psychedelics is the study by Harman et al. (1966). Their subjects included architects, engineers, artists, furniture designers, mathematicians, and physicists. The participants were asked to bring a problem of professional interest to the session that required a creative solution. Sometimes these problems had been creative "log jams" for quite a while. Measures for the subject's creative performance were psychological tests, subjective reports, and validation/acceptance of the finished solution. The dose was 200 mg of mescaline (equivalent to 75 µg LSD), combined with the stimulant methylphenidate. Sessions were conducted in groups of three to four subjects, each subject working alone and in silence, with the other subjects working in different parts of the room. The following tests for creativity were applied:

- The *Purdue Creativity Test* requests the subject to find as many uses as possible for each of a variety of pictured objects. Scores were given for fluency of ideas and range of solutions. Both measures increased, but only fluency increased to a statistically significant degree (+30%).
- The *Miller Objective Visualization Test* asks a subject to envision a two-dimensional outline figure folded into a solid. Most subjects solve these problems by attempting to visualize the figure "in the mind's eye". The mescaline subjects improved significantly in this measure.
- The *Witkin Embedded Figures Test* involves distinguishing a simple geometric figure embedded in a complex coloured figure. All subjects improved significantly on this measure. A shift from field dependence to field independence was demonstrated, a shift that previous research has found to be related to creativity.

The subjective reports showed the impression of more creativity in most subjects, but some reported distractions, e.g. biographical memories. In a closer analysis of the subjective reports, 7 relevant factors have been extracted: 1. a reduction of inhibition and anxiety; 2. the capacity to restructure a problem in a larger context; 3. an enhanced fluency of ideas; 4. a heightened capacity for visual imagery; 5. an increased ability to concentrate; 6. a greater empathy with external processes and objects; 7. an ability to associate dissimilar ideas.

Critical in respect to this study is the additional use of a stimulant (methylphenidate). Amphetamine-like stimulants have no effects with regard to altering the matrix of consciousness, but counteract some effects of psychedelics. Because of this, they were researched by the military to be used as antidotes against psychedelics for making individuals under psychedelics "less autistic" and thoughts and associations more logical and "straight" (cf. Passie & Benzenhöfer 2018).

A study of low-dose LSD and creativity

A rigorously designed scientific study was conducted by Zegane et al. (1967) and sponsored by US National Institute of Mental Health. In a pilot study, it was found that a dose of 1 µg/kg interfered too much with the experiments, so the study used a dose of 0.5 µg per kg bodyweight. Subjects were 31 healthy males, 21 years or older. Nineteen subjects received LSD and eleven did not. Seven tests to specifically measure alterations in creative performance were applied.

A central idea of this study is the hypothesis that there are two styles of psychological and cognitive functioning as conceptualized by Sigmund Freud, the creator of psychoanalysis (Korngold 1963). Freud differentiates two modes of psychological functioning and thinking. The *primary process* is a mode of thinking (and functioning), which stems from an earlier phase of neurocognitive development and is the mode in which children up to the age of 3 years exclusively tend to function. The primary mode is more associative, more imaginative, less abstract, less organized, and much less language-driven. Return to this more primitive mode implies "regression", which is defined as a return to a more primitive mode of thinking (and psychological functioning). Therefore, it represents an ontogenetically earlier mode of thought, which is established quite a while before the *secondary process*. This represents the abstract, logical, critical mode of thought, and a much more differentiated and environment-responsive mode of functioning, usually led by the ego and which functions as reality testing, control of affectivity and thought, to realize an appropriate planning and behavioural response.

It was repeatedly hypothesized in the literature that the primary process might play an essential role in creativity. Therefore the rationale of this experiment was to investigate the ability of some drugs to bring about states that permit primary process contents easier access to consciousness. Interestingly, it was recently shown that the brain matrix necessary to establish the primary process is activated through the 5-HT2A receptor by LSD (Kraehenmann et al. 2017). This regression must, however, be balanced by the retention of certain ego functions which can evaluate and utilize emerging thoughts and feelings for productive ends.

The following tests relevant to creativity were used in the study:

1. Mednick Remote Association Test (RAT). To test the ability to bring remote ideations into associative relationship.

2. The Modified Word Association Test (WAT) to determine whether or not LSD would facilitate an individual's ability to make more creative, less stereotypical responses.

3. Mosaic Design Test. This test was designed specifically for this experiment. The use of mosaic tiles gives the individual the opportunity to create an artistic design. It tests both the ability to conceive interesting patterns, and the capacity to execute his conceptions. Following the completion of the design, each was photographed in colour. The designs were later rated by two judges on a 5-point scale, from 1 (highly disorganized, with minimal imaginative use of materials) through 5 (highly original design of superior organization and aesthetic appeal).

4. Free Association Test (FAT). Each subject was placed by himself in a dimly lit room, where he lay on a comfortable bed. Subjects were instructed to repeat aloud any thoughts that came into their awareness during a subsequent 15-minute interval. Responses were recorded and transcribed. The ability of an individual to give free reign to associations emerging from his preconscious was hypothesized to be intimately related to imaginative exercises involved in creativity.

5. Gottschalk Figure-Perception Test (EFT). This test examines a subject's ability to perceive figures hidden in the general gestalt of a complicated line drawing. It was felt to be useful in determining whether or not a psychotropic drug actually assists an individual in widening his perceptual scope and in perceiving relationships hitherto obliterated by his dependence upon conventional, preconceived figural expectations. The experiment measured numbers of correct answers and mean time taken to reach the correct answer.

6. Tachistoscopic Stimulation. This task was designed to determine whether the latency time for recognition of a word or an object as visually perceived is any shorter for a drug subject than for one who has received a placebo.

The authors found two types of responders to the LSD challenge, which were termed "positive" and "negative reactors". Positive reactors were not overwhelmed by the emergence of material consisting of instinctual impulses and vivid, drive-connected fantasies into conscious awareness. They did not view the experience as being threatening to their sense of ego-intactness, and were able to return to reality-oriented tasks when these were presented. For the most part, the retest scores of the positive reactors showed improvement in creativity-relevant measures. Those who did not like the experience tended to be more threatened, fearing disorganization, and deliberately attempting to control the drug effect. The negative reactors showed no improvement or even a decrease in the retesting. The central feature in which the two groups differed was called "ego-flexibility" by the authors.

Dose	0.5 µg LSD	Placebo
Number of Subjects	20	11
Tests		
RAT (correct)	-0.40	-89
RAT (time)	+3.08	-1.57
WAT (unique)	+0.95	-1.36
WAT (fast)	+0.15	+0.90
WAT (intermediate)	+0.25	-0.45
WAT (slow)	-0.40	-0.45
EFT (correct)	+0.15	+0.55
EFT (time)	-4.96	-2.53
Tachistoscope	+0.50	+0.27
Mosaic Design Test	+0.08	+0.82

Table 18: Mean changes in tests related to creativity (Zegans et al. 1967). Please note: a positive score represents an improvement, or a better score in the second testing; a negative score represents a decrease.

It is obvious from the results in Table 18 that most comparisons were in the predicted direction (subjects under drug do "better" than placebo), but nearly all failed to reach statistical significance, i.e. having a good probability to be produced by chance. Some results were in the opposite direction than predicted. For example, placebo subjects improved more than the drug subjects on their creative mosaic test productions. The only statistically significant difference was in respect to the WAT, where drug subjects were significantly better than placebo at producing unique responses.

The authors conclude that the inconsistencies of the test battery results indicate that a general enhancement did not occur. The most suggestive finding was that LSD may increase the accessibility of remote or unique associations in some subjects. In contrast, the poorest performance was realized by the drugged subjects on tests requiring visual attention (Mosaic Test, EFT, tachistoscope).

The authors were critical about the possibly unconducive laboratory atmosphere, a standardized dose for all subjects (i.e. ignoring individual sensitivity), and a possible irritation effect from the drug in their drug-naïve subjects. They speculate that,

> *greater openness to remote or unique ideas and associations would only be likely to enhance creative thought in those individuals who were meaningfully engaged in some specific interest or problem. There should exist some matrix around which the fluid thought processes can be organized if the experience is not to diffuse into a melange of affective, somatic, and perceptual impressions which may lead to feelings of anxiety or depression". Therefore, the "use of LSD in hopes of improving creative thinking is to be cautioned against.*

A study of creativity with minidoses of psilocybin

Prochazkova et al. (2018) at Leiden University in the Netherlands have conducted an open-label study with the use of dried (psilocybin-containing) mushroom truffles to quantify cognitive-enhancing effects of microdosing. Thirty-eight participants took part in the study, conducted at a recreational drug-taking event in the Netherlands (where these truffles are legal). According to a chemical analysis, 1 gram of the used truffles contained around 16 mg of psilocybin and 1 mg of psilocin. Dependent on bodyweight, the participants took 0.22 gram (ca. 4 mg psilocybin), 0.33 gram (ca 5.7 mg psilocybin) or 0.44 gram (ca. 8 mg psilocybin). The authors rely on Fadiman's definition of microdosing (1/10th to 1/16th of a regular dose), but if a usual dose of psilocybin is considered to be 15-30 mg, it would imply 1.5-3.0 mg or less for a microdose. Given this, the study used minidosing, not microdosing.

Two creativity-related problem-solving tasks were administered before the drug and 1.5 hours after intake. The Picture Concept Task (PCT) is a visual creativity task that involves finding a common association between several images. Performance on the PCT (number of correct responses) was significantly higher under the drug's effect, suggesting an increase of convergent thinking. The Alternate Uses Task (AUT) is used in creativity research to measure divergent thinking performance. During the AUT subjects are presented with a common household object and asked to think of as many possible uses for the object as they can within a limited amount of time. Measured are: number of responses (fluency), number of different categories of responses (frequency), how much the person elaborates on their response (elaboration), and the uniqueness of a response (originality). In respect to fluency, flexibility, originality, drugged subjects showed a better performance, which suggest an increase of divergent thinking (Table 19).

However, it is possible that this performance increase from the first to the second time-point reflects expectation effects (which can be large), learning and possible "relaxation" effects (because of doing the task the second time). Divergent thinking can also benefit from positive mood (Baas et al. 2008). The authors of the study argue that there were also positive effects for convergent thinking, which does not benefit from positive mood. It is noteworthy, that 11 participants were excluded from analysis for the PCT (incorrect understanding of instructions, incomplete tasks) and two for the AUT. It is unclear if the excluded subjects had specific characteristics or if this exclusion might have skewed the results. The authors speculate that psychedelics optimize the balance between cognitive persistence and flexibility.

Measure	Session 1 (pre-drug)	Session 2 (drug)
PCT	6.56 (1.60)	7.59 (1.60)
RPM	8.58 (2.23)	8.97 (1.92)
Flexibility	14.68 (0.99)	16.70 (1.19)
Elaboration	11.20 (0.80)	12.74 (0.93)
Elaboration	2.18 (0.32)	1.76 (0.28)
Originality	12.36 (1.30)	15.67 (1.45)

Table 19: Results of creativity measures with low-dose psilocybin (Prochazkova et al. 2018)

Possible mechanisms of psychedelics and creativity

As this book deals with microdosing and minidosing, the discussion here must focus on possibilities of enhancing creativity through small doses.

It is obvious that higher doses of psychedelics can irritate thoughts, provoke unusual associations, alter perspectives, and enhance imagery. A combination of these factors can further creativity in some subjects, especially when it comes to so-called "log jams in processes of problem-solving" where the creator has fixed thought patterns with respect to a specific problem. This is different from a person who wants to have "more freedom" during the acute effects of the drug to create a work of art such as sculpturing, music, or painting. There might also be processes which can be furthered by some feelings and insights during a psychedelic state, where something can be made of it after the acute effects have waned.

It seems there is not much scientific evidence for the enhancement of creativity during the acute state, but this might be due to the artefacts of restrictive laboratory settings and standardized instruments (e.g. questionnaires, drawing test etc.). Numerous artists have used psychedelics under "uncontrolled conditions" to expand their repertoire and creativity (cf. Masters & Houston 1969, Krippner 1985). Krippner (1983) has recommended that rather than see psychedelics and creativity in a causal relationship, one could view them as being associated. However, most artists and musicians have found that whilst they were incapable of doing good work under the influence of the drug, they could make something creative out of the experience afterwards.

One of the very few "positive" objective findings of the study by Zegans et al. (1967) was that drugged subjects produced more unique and remote word associations. This finding is consistent with studies by Spitzer et al. (1996) and Neiloufar et al. (2016), in which subjects given psilocybin or LSD had more remote word associations. To expand patterns of associations and to gather new perspective on a specific topic can be helpful with creativity, but not necessarily so.

Another possible use of psychedelics is "dynamiting of log jams" in creative problem-solving, as described by Stafford and Golightly (1979). This means that a person is in search of a solution to a problem, but cannot find it, and has become fixed in circling thought patterns. As one subject in the study by Harman et al. (1966) stated: "I dismissed the original idea entirely, and started to approach the graphic problem in a radically different way. That was when things began to happen. All kind of possibilities came to mind". Another subject reported: "Looking at the same problem with (psychedelic) materials, I was able to consider it in a much more basic way, because I could form and keep in mind a much broader picture". An architect, who worked on the design of an arts-and-crafts shopping centre for a resort-university community, experienced the following: "I looked at the paper I was to draw on. It was completely blank ... Suddenly I saw the finished project. I did some quick calculations ... it would fit on the property and ... would meet the costs ... It was contemporary architecture with the richness of a cultural heritage. ... I completed four sheets of fairly comprehensive sketches." However, these were experiences under a moderate, not miniscule (i.e. not micro), dose of a psychedelic drug, and which was also combined with a stimulant.

Besides breaking log jams, there might be a second kind of creativity-enhancing effect of low doses. Recently I came across a person who had a "creativity experience" with a (verified) dose of 15 µg LSD. This male academic in his 30s reported:

> *I had thought about meditation as a possible method for gaining insights, in the philosophical context, that might enable intuitive—and therefore as yet unknown— connections to emerge. With this in mind, lying down and starting from a basic meditation exercise, I entered into a state of 'receiving' aphorisms that emerged, of the kind I have already frequently written about. The resulting sentences/aphorisms are, of course, not all truly profound, but they fascinated me with regard to the process by which they arose. I noticed in amazement how a sentence, starting from the first word—at which point I still had no idea of the direction in which the sentence was heading—would unfold, word by word, right to the end without any help from me and would present itself to me as a virtually complete sentence. In the process, I experienced the 'creative rush' as an act of effortless observation. With ease, grammatical structures seemed to develop of their own accord, simultaneously carrying with them content that was*

new and unfamiliar to me. The sentences arose, with
short breaks for recalling them and writing them down,
over the course of approximately one hour. During the
creative state, I was in an emotionally balanced and
calm to slightly excited mood, which I experienced as
positive; at the same time, I felt unusually rational and
clear.

Interestingly, in spite of the hype on microdosing for enhancement of creativity, this kind of detailed description cannot be found on internet platforms, where statements are limited to just one or two short sentences. It was the psychiatrist Hanscarl Leuner at Göttingen University in Germany who conceptualized the "psychotoxic basic syndrome" of which the "increased production of inner stimuli" is an integral part of the drug's effect on the brain. For higher doses, Krippner (1969: 272) has put it this way: "Psychedelic substances seem to affect consciousness in such a way that the nervous system is flooded with external and internal stimuli". Enhanced imagery and synaesthesias are parts of this increased stimuli production. In view of this, one could easily think of the description above as an effect resulting from a mild change in this respect, i.e. a slightly increased production of inner stimuli, which leads to a subtle furthering of the flow of thoughts and fantasies.

As a third possibility one might evaluate the long-term effects on creativity, but as far as I can see, there is virtually no evidence for this, not even any internet-based subjective reports that give trustworthy evidence for this kind of effect.

Possible neurophysiological mechanisms

With respect to neurophysiological mechanisms related to creative problem-solving one has to consider the results of recent brain-imaging studies on the hallucinogens. These have shown alterations of metabolism, especially increased activity in the regions of the thalamus, the frontal cortex, and the right hemisphere (Vollenweider et al. 1997). Another level of brain activity can be measured by investigating the interaction of certain brain areas and their concerted activity in relation to specific tasks (or without a task). This specific connectivity of brain areas working together is called "functional connectivity", which provides a set of interacting regions in the brain for specific functions. It has been shown recently that psychedelics like LSD or psilocybin alter the structure and the concerted interaction of those networks (Carhart-Harris et al. 2016, Mueller et al. 2018). These changes are likely to contribute to the alterations of sensory perception, affectivity, self-experience and imagery. Alterations of the interaction of the brain's networks can also easily explain experiences of "new perspectives" under the influence of psychedelics (e.g. Tagliazucci et al. 2016, Gasser et al. 2015). Another result of concerted changes in brain functioning is the weakening or even elimination of conceptual cognition, i.e. the building of more or less abstract concepts of things in our minds upon which we operate. This change in conceptual cognition might be especially helpful with the above described creative log jams—by not allowing one to proceed with one's usual ruminations about the problem. Then again, these results have only been achieved with much higher doses (in the range of 100–200 µg LSD) which cannot easily be used to predict changes with low or very low doses. It is probable that the described changes in brain functioning occur only with much higher doses and that a certain dose level is needed to cause these changes. Therefore it seems reasonable to conclude that changes in brain functioning brought about by miniscule doses are far less influential (and are likely to have another structure) than are those induced by moderate to high doses of psychedelics.

15

Microdosing Other Psychedelics

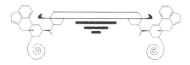

Not much is known about taking low doses or microdoses of other psychedelics, especially on a regular basis. Fadiman (2016) collected a few self-reports on different substances. However, more than a few hints of information on microdosing are known with regard to psilocybin and mescaline. Therefore, in this chapter I will limit my presentation to these two substances.

The general equivalence of the effects or "clinical syndromes" of LSD, psilocybin and mescaline have been proven in different studies (cf. Hollister 1968). It would seem, then, that there might be no big difference when taking one or the other of these "classic psychedelics" for microdosing. However, one must keep in mind that these substances do have a different duration of effects (cf. Diagram 24) and different patterns of receptor interactions, despite the fact that their major target, the 5-HT2A receptor, seems to be identical.

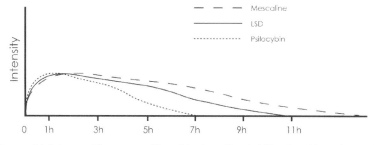

Diagram 24: Scheme of the course of the clinical reactions to LSD, psilocybin and mescaline

Here, I will discuss a few important pharmacological facts about psilocybin and mescaline. Readers who are interested in more details are referred to another review which provides essential pharmacological data about these substances (Passie & Halpern 2014).

Psilocybin

Psilocybin was isolated from *Psilocybe spp.* mushrooms and synthesized by Swiss chemist Albert Hofmann in 1958. Psilocybin is extremely non-toxic and has only mild physiological effects, which are usually well tolerated (Passie et al. 2003). Doses of psilocybin which are 100 times higher than those used by humans have been given to different species of animals without inducing any detectable damage (Weidmann et al. 1958). Virtually nothing is known about the long-term effects of a regular intake of psilocybin. In contrast to LSD, there have been no studies on this practice.

In an experiment to induce tolerance, Hollister gave psilocybin every day for 21 days starting with 1.5 mg and finishing with 27 mg on the last day. On the twenty-second day there was hardly any reaction to a dose of 15 mg (Hollister 1961). However, in another study it was found that tolerance to psilocybin did not develop as completely as did direct tolerance to LSD. It was also found that subjects tolerant to LSD were completely tolerant to psilocybin, but those tolerant to psilocybin were not as cross-tolerant to a challenging dose of LSD (Isbell et al. 1961).

Sercl et al. (1961) conducted trials with very low doses of psilocybin. In these observational studies, only the experimental subjects were blind to the drug or placebo conditions, but not the researchers, which can seriously bias results. The first investigation used fifteen healthy volunteers, of which five were dosed with 1–2 mg psilocybin by mouth. Four subjects experienced euphoria, mydriasis, and face hyperemia. Ten healthy subjects were dosed with 3–6 mg by subcutaneous injection. Seven experienced mild euphoria, increased reflexes, and finger tremor. Some found the reaction unpleasant with strange thoughts, difficulties in concentrating, tiredness, and occasional inadequate happiness. Placebo had no effect on the same subjects, although one experienced mild euphoria. A second experiment investigated reactions to low doses of psilocybin (1–2 mg per os, 3 mg s.c.) in patients suffering from organic brain disease (e.g. multiple sclerosis), who had developed depressive mood as a reaction to their organic disease. The drug was given daily for ten days. Eight of those patients developed euphoria whilst seven did not experience any effects. In another experiment, neurotic patients received the same dosage regime. Eight subjects developed euphoria, sometimes strong, some experienced sensory enhancement. Two had very mild primitive pseudohallucinatory phenomena. Mild hyperreflexia was typical, but three patients were without any neurological effects.

Parenteral application lead to stronger effects, with shorter onset. With longer application over up to ten days days no evidence for any tolerance or diminished effects was found.

The authors report that the euphoric mood state was very helpful in the psychotherapy with these patients. The mindset or attitude towards the neurosis changes to their advantage. Individual sensitivity to the drug was obvious. In general, neurotic patients exhibit a greater sensitivity for psilocybin's effects. No withdrawal effects were observed. Because of the negligible side effects of the very low doses the authors think that psilocybin can be given also to outpatients.

Some reports from "microdosers" using psilocybin can be found on the internet. They sound like this:

> In general, a tiny dose of psilocybin makes me think
> much more deeply in every aspect of my life. Instead of
> having a monkey mind, creating noise, my mind is still.
> ... Psilocybin makes me feel exactly how I felt when I
> was a kid in school. It is happiness, because you realize
> that you have all you need. During my test days I felt
> more love for myself, and I can give that to others. ...
> My cravings for sugar, smoke and sodas nearly went
> away. I wanted to give my body the best fuel, I feel like
> I attract positive people and happenings in my life.
> (quoted in Fadiman 2016:58)

There are also less positive reports. A person who took a very low, sub-perceptual dose of mushrooms) every 4th day for 10 doses wrote:

> The day of and the day after dose days I felt disconnected
> when engaging with people. I was drawn to pull back
> and not engage as fully as I normally would. Felt a bit

out of sorts in relation to my community and others.
The day after a dose day I usually did not feel good.
Some days worse than others. This is normal for me to
have days where I don't feel good, but these were more
frequent ... I am more connected to my intuitive self and
more trusting the information I am receiving. ... I see
and own my personal value and worth like I have never
known it before. I have seen how certain behaviors and
belief systems have contributed to low self-esteem and
low self-worth patterns.
(Quoted in Fadiman 2016: 59)

Both descriptions sound more like a "perceptible", above-threshold experience with psilocybin. But because psilocybin is very hard to synthesize, one cannot buy synthetic psilocybin which means that one has to take psilocybin-containing mushrooms. It is hard to evaluate how much psilocybin these mushrooms actually contain. Therefore, dosing with psilocybin mushrooms implies serious uncertainties with exact dosing. This problem is less relevant when usual recreational doses in the of range of 10–30 mg (psilocybin) are taken, but are important when it comes to microdosing.

In a letter to Hanscarl Leuner, a European pioneer in hallucinogens and psycholytic therapy, dated December 22nd, 1959, two doctors from the German Department of the Sandoz Company reported "that the administration of 3 mg parenteral or 6 mg per os psilocybin causes a state of euphoric indifference/ unconcern. The patient is psychologically and physiologically relaxed and feels himself far away from sorrows of every day". Sandoz doctors arranged for a therapeutic use of very low doses of psilocybin (ranging from 2 times 0.5 mg daily up to 3 times 2 mg daily). They reported "some quite remarkable successes seen with this treatment" (Augsbrunner and Hammerschmidt 1959: 2). However, it is unknown if these experiments were followed by clinical trials.

Abramson and Rolo (1967) tested subjective reactions to low doses of LSD and psilocybin. Subjects had to detect lower doses. The experiments were run blind or double-blind in groups of six subjects. The same six subjects were repeatedly dosed with either LSD, psilocybin, congeners of LSD or placebo. Some subjects in the group received placebo while others received the drugs. Table 20 provides an overview of the doses and the estimates as given by the subjects.

Psilocybin dose	Number of trials	Correct estimate	False estimate	Remarks
2 mg	8	8		"Threshold dose"
3 mg	4	3	1	
4 µg	19	19		"25 µg LSD"
6 mg	19	18	1	"25 µg LSD" "35 µg LSD" "25–50 µg LSD"
8 mg	14	13	1	"75 µg LSD"
Placebo	22	8	4	2x Low dose psilocybin estimated

Table 20: Number of trials and guesses/estimates by six "placebo-negative" subjects (Abramson and Rolo 1967)

It seems astonishing how often the subjects were right in their assessment of the dose received. To frame this, it is important to know that the experiments were conducted on "a group of 6 essentially placebo negative subjects", i.e. subjects who consistently did not react significantly to placebo in a lot of previous drug experiments. The subjects had a lot of previous drug experiences and some had taken part in similar experiments before.

The authors had also evaluated statistically at which dose level the subjects were able to detect any effect. As Table 21 demonstrates, the subject's dose levels showed little variation. These results have been confirmed by another study, in which the minimum dose at which "definite changes" could be perceived has been found to be about 6 µg psilocybin per kg bodyweight (Hollister 1967: 40).

Subject 1	3.6
Subject 2	3.1
Subject 3	3.1
Subject 4	3.4
Subject 5	3.6
Subject 6	3.6

Table 21: The threshold dose of psilocybin in mg calculated on the basis of 25 µg of LSD as the threshold from subjects' estimates (Abramson and Rolo 1967)

In a study by Fanciullacci et al. (1974) the hypothesis that headache sufferers were more sensitive to drugs interacting with the serotonin system was investigated. The two experimental groups consisted of 30 healthy normal

subjects and 36 migraine sufferers. All subjects were dosed every 3 days at
9:00 am in a double-blind randomized scheme with an oral dose of 20 µg/
kg psilocybin. Subjects were "questioned about their sensations" at 4, 8 and
12 hours after drug administration. Three categories for reactions were used
(1 = no reaction; 2 = simple psycho-affective reactions; 3 = psycho-affective
reaction plus perceptual alterations). In response to the given dosage 86% of
the normal subjects reported "no reaction", and 14% reaction of category 1.
No subject reported a reaction of category 2. The headache sufferers showed
reactions of category 0 and 1 in 41%, and of category 2 in 18% of subjects
(Diagram 25).

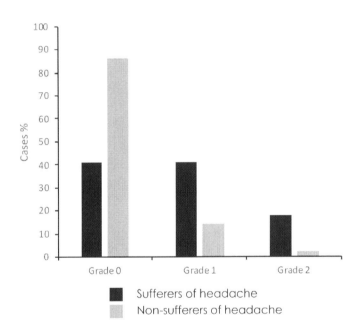

Diagram 25: Psilocybin, when administered to migraine-headache sufferers provokes a
more psychic effect than in normal subjects (Fanciullacci et al. 1974)

A few early studies in which psilocybin was used as an adjunct to
psychotherapy, doses of 3–15 mg were given. Unfortunately, these studies
did not report on the effects of different doses (review in Passie 2005).

Mescaline

Mescaline has to be taken in much larger amounts (350–500 mg for a full dose) than LSD or psilocybin and is known to have more effects on the physiology of the human organism. These effects consist of a mild stimulation, associated with an increase in blood pressure and pulse rate. There have been no reported cases of relevant toxicity of mescaline in humans.

The first information of a threshold dose for mescaline has been reported by Marshall (1937: 290), who found that with mescaline sulphate "up to doses of 0.05 gm. no distinct symptoms were produced". According to this author, a little above this threshold visual perception is altered and afterimages are prolonged.

Not much is known about the long-term effects of repeated dosing of mescaline on a day to day basis. In contrast to LSD or psilocybin, there have been no studies done in this respect. However, monkeys have been fed with mescaline in experiments by the US Army for several months. The monkeys were found "to tolerate very large doses after a while" (Marazzi 1954). As with repeated dosing, there is not much known about the development of tolerance with mescaline. Interestingly, in some animal experiments no development of tolerance was reported (Speck 1957).

Psychedelic pioneer Bernard Copley was the first to report on microdosing with mescaline. During the 1950s, Copley did regular self-experiments, some with unusual dosing strategies. In one experiment he took a daily dose of 50 mg of mescaline for sixty days. He found that "on certain days, if I had eaten a little more food than usual or was a little fatigued, I could not tell that I had taken it at all. On other days when the energy cycle was higher than ordinary, or when I ate little or nothing, it almost reached the point where I would not want to carry on daily work or contact with people. The sensation of the small dose is just one of well-being" (Copley 1962: 17). Interestingly, Copley did not experience any tolerance during his 60-day experiment, which might point to a different development of tolerance with small doses.

In a carefully done and extensive study, Kreppel (1964) has investigated "phenomena at the threshold level of mescaline" (his dissertation's title). He administered doses of 60–90 mg of mescaline by mouth and found that two groups of subjects can be distinguished: the "weak reactors" and the "strong reactors". Both groups showed a lot of psychophysical symptoms, including an urge to move and talk, slowing of reactions, tendency to fall asleep, changes in time experience, headaches, feelings of an empty stomach, pulse acceleration, tinnitus, salivation and enhanced sensory sensitivity. In some psychometric and neuropsychological tests, measures relevant for creativity were used, but no positive effect on these measures were detected.

As I described in the history chapter, soccer fans in Peru are reported to have used lower doses of mescaline for recreational purposes at soccer games. Coming across this information, Keeper Trout did some experiments with low doses of mescaline in the early 1980s by using "sub-tripping amounts of San Pedro" as a hiking aid. He found these effects greatly enhanced the hiking experience, but did not give him more energy. However, "... there was a sense of stimulation but there was also a sense of distraction that balanced or functionally negated it" (Trout 2018).

In a recent internet entry, a certain Techlos describes his experiments with mescaline microdosing.

> *I experimented microdosing with mescaline from a* pachanoii/bridgesii *hybrid for a week a few years ago. Has a similar energetic alertness to LSD, but it's less mental and more physical. It was like I knew exactly what my body was capable of, and there was no way to make a mistake. I went for a bike ride, and ended up doing my usual 30 min track in 17 minutes. I wasn't even out of breath at the end... what happened was my form improved immensely. I knew exactly how to push the pedals to get the most out of my movements, and how hard to push to ensure I didn't wear myself out. I could feel the wind brush past me so strongly, that I took an aerodynamic position almost by reflex. It's hard to describe exactly, but I knew everything I needed to do to fucking tear down the bike path.*
> (Techlos 2014)

In sum, there is not much research and experience in respect to microdosing with psychedelics other than LSD, but it cannot be excluded that these may have their own worth and applications.

References

Abraham HD, Duffy FH (1996): Stable qEEG differences in post-LSD visual disorder by split half analyses: Evidence for disinhibition. *Psychiatry Research: Neuroimaging*, 67: 173–187

Abraham HD, Duffy, FH (2001): EEG coherence in post-LSD visual hallucinations. *Psychiatry Research: Neuroimaging*, 107: 151–163

Abramson HA (1955) Lysergic acid diethylamide (LSD25): III. As an adjunct to psychotherapy with elimination of fear of homosexuality. *Journal of Psychology* 39: 127–155

Abramson HA (ed.) (1967) *The use of LSD in psychotherapy and alcoholism.* New York, Kansas City: Bobbs Merrill

Abramson HA, Jarvik ME, Hirsch MW (1955a) Lysergic acid diethylamide (LSD25): VII. Effect upon two measures of motor performance. *J Psychol* 39: 455–464

Abramson HA, Jarvik ME, Hirsch MW (1955b) Lysergic acid diethylamide (LSD-25): X. Effect on reaction time to auditory and visual stimuli. *J Psychol* 40: 39–52

Abramson HA, Jarvik ME, Hirsch MW, Ewald A (1955c) Lysergic acid diethylamide (LSD25): V. Effect on spatial relations abilities. *J Psychol* 39: 435–442

Abramson HA, Jarvik ME, Kaufman MR, Kornetsky C, Wagner M (1955d) Lysergic Acid Diethylamide (LSD-25): I. Physiological and perceptual responses. *J Psychol* 39: 3–60

Abramson HA, Jarvik ME, Levine A, Kaufman MR, Hirsch MW (1955e) Lysergic acid diethylamide (LSD-25): XV. The effects produced by substitution of a tap water placebo. *J Psychol* 40: 367–383

Abramson HA, Kornetsky C, Jarvik ME, Kaufman MR, Ferguson MW (1955f) Lysergic acid diethylamide (LSD-25): XI. Content analysis of clinical reactions. *J Psychol* 40: 53–60

Abramson HA, Waxenberg SE, Levine A, Kaufman MR, Kornetsky C (1955g) Lysergic acid diethylamide (LSD-25): XIII Effect on Bender-Gestalt test performance. *J Psychol* 40: 341–349

Abramson HA (1956) Lysergic Acid Diethylamide (LSD-25): XIX. As an adjunct to brief psychotherapy, with special reference to ego enhancement. *J Psychol* 199–229

Abramson HA, Jarvik ME, Gorin MH, Hirsch MW (1956) Lysergic Acid Diethylamide (LSD-25): XVII. Tolerance development and its relationship to a Theory of Psychosis. *J Psychol* 41: 81–105

Abramson HA, Sklarofsky B, Baron MO, Fremont-Smith N (1957) Production of tolerance to psychosis-producing doses of lysergic acid diethylamide. *Science* 126: 1020

Abramson HA, Sklarofsky B, Baron MO, Fremont-Smith N (1958) Lysergic acid diethylamide (LSD-25) antagonists. II. Development of tolerance in man to LSD-25 by prior administration of MLD-41 (1-methyl-d-lysergic acid diethylamide). *AMA Arch Neurol Psychiat* 79: 201–207

Abramson HA (1959) Lysergic Acid Diethylamide (LSD-25): XXIX. The Response Index as a Measure of Threshold Activity of Psychotropic Drugs in Man. *J Psychol* 48: 65–78

Abramson HA (ed.) (1960a) *The use of LSD in Psychotherapy*. New York: Josiah Macy Foundation

Abramson (1960b) Discussion. In: Abramson (ed.) *The use of LSD in psychotherapy*. New York: Josiah Macy Foundation. 44

Abramson HA (1960c) Lysergic Acid Diethylamide (LSD-25): XXX. the Questionnaire Technique with Notes on its Use. *J Psychol* 49: 57–65

Abramson HA (1960d) Lysergic acid diethylamide (LSD-25). XXXI. Comparison by questionnaire of psychotomimetic activity of congeners on normal subjects and drug addicts. *J Ment Sci* 106: 1120–1123

Abramson HA, Rolo A, Stache J (1960a) Lysergic acid diethylamide (LSD-25) antagonists: chlorpromazine. *J Neuropsychiatr* 1: 307–310

Abramson HA, Rolo A, Sklarofsky B, Stache J (1960b) Production of cross-tolerance to psychosis-producing doses of lysergic acid diethylamide and psilocybin. *J Psychol* 49: 151–154

Abramson HA (ed.) (1967) *The use of LSD in psychotherapy and alcoholism*. Indianapolis, New York, Kansas City: Bobbs Merrill

Abramson H, Rolo A (1967) Comparison of LSD with methysergide and psilocybin on test subjects. *J Asthma Res* 3: 81–96

Aghajanian GK (1994) Electrophysiological studies on the actions of hallucinogenic drugs at 5-HT2 receptors in rat brain. *NIDA Res Monogr* 146: 183–202

Alboni, S, van Dijk, RM, Poggini, S. (2017) Fluoxetine effects on molecular, cellular and behavioral endophenotypes of depression are driven by the living environment. *Mol Psychiatry* 22: 552–561

Andersohn F, Garbe E (2009). "Cardiac and noncardiac fibrotic reactions caused by ergot-and nonergot-derived dopamine agonists". *Movement Disorders* 24: 129–133

Anderson EW, Rawnsley K (1954) Clinical studies of lysergic acid diethylamide. *Mschr Psychiat Neurol* 128: 38–55

Andersson M, Persson M, Kjellgren A (2017) Psychoactive substances as a last resort—a qualitative study of self-treatment of migraine and cluster headaches. *Harm Reduction Journal* 201714:60, available at https://harmreductionjournal.biomedcentral.com/articles/10.1186/s12954-017-0186-6, accessed 01-01-2018

Andrade R (2011) Serotonergic regulation of neuronal excitability in the prefrontal cortex. *Neuropharmacology* 61: 382–386

Anonymous (2015) Comments on microdosing. Available at https://www.reddit.com/r/Drugs/comments/2sgtfj/question_about_low_dose_4050ug_lsd/, accessed 25-12-2017

Anonymous (2015) Just hit tab: why Silicon Valley techies are dropping LSD at work. Available at https://www.theguardian.com/science/shortcuts/2015/nov/29/silicon-valley-techies-dropping-lsd-at-work, accessed 25-01-2018

Anonymous (2017) Microdosing and pupil dilation. Available at http://microdosing.info/microdosing-pupil-dilation/, accessed 12-23-2017

Anonymous (2017) What is Microdosing and What are Proposed Benefits? September 29, 2017, available at https://www.purenootropics.net/beginners-guide-to-microdosing-psychedelics/, accessed 25-12-2017

Arieti S (1976) *Creativity: the magic synthesis*. New York: Basic Books

Arnold OH, Hoff H (1953) Untersuchungen über die Wirkungsweise von Lysergsäurediäthylamid. *Wiener Z Nervenheilk* 6: 129

Augsberger, Hammerschmidt (1959) Letter to Hanscarl Leuner, dated December 22, 1959

Austin P (2016a) *A quick guide to microdosing psychedelics.* Amazon ebook

Austin P (2016b) Statement, quoted in: Grob Plante (2016)

Austin (2017a) What is microdosing? Available at https://thethirdwave.co/whats-the-deal-with-microdosing/, accessed 03-03-2018

Austin P (2017b) *The Essential Guide To LSD Microdosing.* Available at https://thethirdwave.co/microdosing-with-lsd/, accessed 25-12-2017

Austin P (2017c) Third Wave Survey Respondents. Available at https://thethirdwave.co/category/microdosing/, accessed 04-04-2018

Austin P (2018) *Microdosing psychedelics: a practical guide to upgrade your life.* Amazon

Axelrod J, Brady RO, Witkop B, Evarts EV (1957) *The distribution and metabolism of LSD.* Ann NY Acad Sci 66: 435–444

Baas M, De Dreu CKW, Nijstad BA (2008) A meta-analysis of 25 years of mood-creativity research: hedonic tone, activation, or regulatory focus? *Psychol Bull* 134: 779–806

Barron F (1963) *Creativity and psychological health.* Princeton, New Jersey: Van Nostrand

Bartlett FC (1932) *Remembering.* Cambridge: Cambridge University Press

Becker AM (1949) Zur Psychopathologie der Lysergsäurediäthylamidwirkung. *Wiener Z Nervenhk* 2: 402–440

Bender L (1946) *Instructions for the Use of the Visual Motor Gestalt Test.* New York: Amer Orthopsychiatric Association

Bender L, Sankar DVS (1968) Chromosome damage not found in leukocytes of children treated with LSD-25. *Science* 159: 749

Benedetti F (2008) *Placebo effects.* Oxford, New York: Oxford University Press

Bente D, Itil T, Schmid EE (1957) Electroencephalic studies concerning the action of LSD-25. *EEG Clin Neurophysiol* 9: 359

Berlin L, Guthrie T, Weider A, Goodell H, Wolff HG (1955) Studies in human cerebral function: the influence of mescaline and lysrgic acid on cerebral processes pertinent to creative activity. *J Nerv Ment Dis* 122: 487–491

Bewellbuzz (2016) LSD Microdosing boosts workplace productivity. May 21, 2016, available at https://www.bewellbuzz.com/medicinal-mushroom/lsd-microdosing-workplace-productivity/, accessed 25-12-2017

Blacker KH, Jones RT, Stone GC, Pfefferbaum D (1968) Chronic Users of LSD: The "Acidheads". *Am J Psychiatry* 125: 341–351

Blewett D, Chwelos N (undated [ca. 1960]) *Handbook for the therapeutic use of lysergic acid diethylamide*. Regina, Canada: self-published

Bliss EL, Clark LD, West CD (1959) Studies of sleep deprivation – relationship to schizophrenia. *AMA Arch Neur Psychiat* 81: 348–359

Bodmer I (1999) *Erinnerung an einen aussergewöhnlichen Bewusstseinszustand.* Berlin: VWB

Bonson KR, Buckholtz JW, Murphy DL (1996) Chronic administration of serotonergic antidepressants attenuates the subjective effects of LSD in humans. *Neuropsychopharmacology* 14: 425–436

Bonson KR, Murphy DL (1996) Alterations in response to LSD in humans associated with chronic administration of tricyclic antidepressants, monoamine oxidase inhibitors or lithium. *Behav Brain Res*: 73: 229–233

Boyd ES, Rothlin E, Bonner JF, Slater JH, Hodge HC (1955) Preliminary studies of the metabolism of LSD using radioactive carbon-marked molecules. *J Nerv Ment Dis* 122: 470–471

Brodwin E (2017) Scientists are about to find out how Silicon Valley's LSD habit really affects productivity. Available at http://www.businessinsider.de/microdosing-lsd-effects-risks-science-2017-6?r=US&IR=T, accessed 01-01-2018

Buchborn T (2018) Mail to Torsten Passie, 02-12-2018

Buchborn T (2018) Personal communication

Buchborn T, Schröder H, Dieterich DC, Grecksch G, Höllt V (2014) Tolerance to LSD and DOB induced shaking behavior: Differential adaptions of frontocortical 5-HT2A and glutamate receptor binding sites. *Behav Brain Res* 281: 62–68

Buchborn T, Grecksch G, Dieterich DC, Höllt V (2016) Tolerance to lysergic acid diethylamide: overview, correlates, and clinical implications. In: Preedy VR (ed.) *Neuropathology of Drug Addictions and Substance Misuse: Volume 2*. New York: Academic Press, pp. 846–858

Buckman J (1967) Theoretical aspects of L.S.D. therapy. *Int J Social Psychiatry* 13: 126–138

Buettner G (1969) *Die Provozierbarkeit der Wirkung von Lysergsäurediäthylamid (LSD-25) durch Placebogaben.* Munich, Germany: Max-Planck-Institut für Psychiatrie, Medical dissertation

Busch AK, Johnson WC (1950) LSD 25 as an aid in psychotherapy. *Dis Nerv System* 11: 241–243

Bye RA (1979) Hallucinogenic plants of the Tarahumara. *J Ethnopharmacology* 1: 23–48

Cahal R (n.d. [2016]) *Microdosing: Improve your energy, mood, and productivity with psychedelics.* Poland: Amazon Books on demand

Camara BS, Camara F, Berthe,A, Oswald A (2013) Micro-dosing of fertilizer – a technology for farmers' needs and resources. *International Journal of AgriScience* 3: 387–399

Canamo – La Revista de la Cultura del Cannabis (2004) *Musica y drogas* [Special issue]. Barcelona: Canamo

Carhart-Harris R, Nutt DJ (2017) Serotonin and brain function: a tale of two receptors. *J Psychopharm* 31: 1091–1120

Carhart-Harris RL, Bolstridge M, Rucker J, Day CMJ, Erritzoe D, Kaelen M, Bloomfield M, Rickard JA, Forbes B, Feilding A, Taylor D, Pilling S, Curran VH, Nutt DJ (2016b) Psilocybin with psychological support for treatment- resistant depression: An open-label feasibility study. *Lancet Psychiatry* 3: 619–627

Carhart-Harris RL Erritzoe D, Williams T, Stone JM, Reed LJ, Colasanti A, Tyacke RJ, Leech R, Malizia AL, Murphy K, Hobden P, Evans J, Feilding A, Wise RG, Nutt DJ (2012) Neural correlates of the psychedelic state as determined by fMRI studies with psilocybin. *Proc Natl Acad Sci* U. S. A. 109: 2138–2143

Carhart-Harris RL, Muthukumaraswamy S, Roseman L, Kaelen M, Droog W, Murphy K, Tagliazucchi E, Schenberg EE, Nest T, Orban C, Leech R, Williams LT, Williams TM, Bolstridge M, Sessa B, McGonigle J, Sereno MI, Nichols D, Hellyer PJ, Hobden P, Evans J, Singh KD, Wise RG, Curran HV, Feilding A, Nutt DJ (2016a) Neural correlates of the LSD experience revealed by multimodal neuroimaging. *Proc Nat Acad Sci* U.S.A. 113: 4853–4858

Carlino E, Benedetti F, Pollo A (2014) The effects of manipulating verbal instructions on physical performance. *Zeitschrift für Psychologie* 222: 154–64

Chlodwig R (2016) The hypnosophic mystery of the psychedelic Israeli Connection. Available at https://aryanskynet.wordpress.com/2016/11/26/the-hypnosophic-mystery-of-the-psychedelic-israeli-connection/, accessed 11-20-2017

Cholden L, Kurland A, Savage C (1955) Clinical reactions and tolerance to LSD in chronic schizophrenia. *J Nerv Ment Dis* 122: 211–221

Clark LD, Bliss EL (1957) Psychopharmacological studies of lysergic acid diethylamide (LSD-25) intoxication. *Arch Neurol Psychiatr* 78: 653–655

Clark LD, Clark LS (1956) The effects of cortisone on LSD-25 intoxication in schizophrenics patients. *J Nerv Ment Dis* 125: 561–562

Cohen MM, Marinello MJ, Back N (1967) Chromosomal damage in human leukocytes induced by lysergic acid diethylamide. *Science* 155: 1417–1419

Cohen MM, Mukherjee AB (1968) Meiotic chromosome damage induced by LSD-25. *Nature* 219: 1072–1074

Cohen S (1960) Lysergic acid diethylamide: side effects and complications. *J Nerv Ment Dis* 130: 30–40

Cohen S, Krippner S (1985) (eds.) LSD in retrospect. *J Psychoactive Drugs* 17: 213–303

Cohen S, Krippner S (1985) Editors' introduction. *J Psychoactive Drugs* 17: 213–217

Colloca L, Klinger R, Flor H, Bingel U (2013) Placebo analgesia: psychological and neurobiological mechanisms. *Pain* 154: 511–514

Combes RD, Berridge T, Connelly J, Eve MD, Garner RC, Toon S, Wilcox P (2003) Early microdose drug studies in human volunteers can minimise animal testing: Proceedings of a workshop organised by Volunteers in Research and Testing. *Eur J Pharm Sci* 19: 1–11

Condrau G (1949) Klinische Erfahrungen mit Lysergsäurediäthylamid an Geisteskranken. *Acta Psychiat Neurol* 24: 9–32

Conrad C (1958) *Die beginnende Schizophrenie.* Stuttgart: Thieme

Copley B (1962) *Hallucinogenic drugs and their use in extra-sensory perception.* Joshua Tree, CA: Hypnosophic Institute

Cruz RW (2016) *Microdosing LSD: The definitive guide to increased creativity and productivity.* New York: Open Book Publishing

De Maar EWJ, Williams HL, Miller AI, Pfeiffer CC (1960) Effects in man of single and combined oral doses of reserpine, iproniazid, and d-lysergic acid diethylamide. *Clin Pharmacol Therap* 1: 23–30

Deimel C (1980) *Tarahumara: Indianer im Norden Mexikos.* Frankfurt/Main: Syndikat

Delay J, Pichot P (1951) Diethylamide de l'acide d-lysergique et troubles psychiques de l'ergotism. *Comptes Rendues Societe de Biologique* 145: 1609

DeMaar EWJ, Williams HL, Miller AI, Pfeiffer CC (1960) Effects in man of single and combined oral doses of reserpine, iproniazid and LSD. *Clin Pharmacol Ther* 1: 23–30

Denton M (2017) Microdosing LSD: The ultimate creativity nootropic and how to make it right. Available at https://www.youtube.com/watch?v=TFiqNZXWN7g, accessed 01-01-2018

Diaz J-L, Huttunen MO (1971) Persistent increase in brain serotonin turnover after chronic administration of LSD in the rat. *Science* 174: 62–64

Dihotsky NI, Loughman WD, Mogar RE, Lipscomb WR (1971) LSD and genetic damage. *Science* 172: 431–447

Dobkin de Rios M, Janiger O (2010) *LSD, spirituality and the creative process.* Rochester, VT: Park Street Press

Dolder PC, Schmid Y, Haschke M, Rentsch KM, Liechti ME (2015) Pharmacokinetics and Concentration-Effect Relationship of Oral LSD in Humans. *Int J Neuropsychopharmacol* 19(1). pii: pyv072. doi: 10.1093/ijnp/pyv072.

Dolder PC, Schmid Y, Müller F, Borgwardt S, Liechti ME (2016) LSD Acutely Impairs Fear Recognition and Enhances Emotional Empathy and Sociality. *Neuropsychopharmacology* 41: 2638–2646

Dolder PC, Schmid Y, Steuer AE, Kraemer T, Rentsch KM, Hammann F et al (2017) Pharmacokinetics and pharmacodynamics of lysergic acid diethylamide in healthy subjects. *Clin Pharmacokinetics* (e-pub ahead of print; doi:10.1007/s40262- 017-0513-9)

Dorrance DL, Janiger O, Teplitz RL (1975) Effect of peyote on human chromosomes. Cytogenetic study of the Huichol Indians of Northern Mexico. *J American Medical Association* 234: 299–302

Durden T (2017) Silicon Valley millennial offers LSD "microdosing" course, but is there a hidden agenda? October 6, 2017, available at http://www.zerohedge.com/news/2017-10-05/silicon-valley-millennial-offers-lsd-microdosing-course-there-hidden-agenda, accessed 25-12-2017

Durr RA (1970) *Poetic vision and psychedelic experience*. Syracuse, NY: Syracuse University Press

Dyck E (2005) Flashback: psychiatric experimentation with LSD in historical perspective. *Canadian J Psychiat* 50: 381–388

Eisner BG (1960) Discussion. In: Abramson HA (ed.) *The use of LSD in psychotherapy*. New York: Josiah Macy Jr. Foundation,. 45

Eisner BG, Cohen S (1958): Psychotherapy with Lysergic Acid Diethylamide. *J Nerv Ment Dis* 127: 528–539

Elkes J, Elkes C, Bradley PB (1954) The effect of some drugs on the electrical activity of the brain and on behaviour. *J Ment Sci* 100: 125–128

EMA (2004) Position Paper on nonclinical safety studies to support clinical trials with a single microdose. European Medicines Agency (EMA), committee for medicinal products for human use (CHMP). Available at http://www.emea.europa.eu/pdfs/human/swp/259902 en.pdf

Fanciulacci M, Del Bene E, Franchi G, Sicuteri F (1977) Phantom limb pain: sub-hallucinogenic treatment with lysergic acid diethylamide (LSD-25). *Headache* 17: 118–119

Fischer R, Fox R, Ralstin M (1972) Creative performance and the hallucinogenic drug-induced experience. *J Psychedelic Drugs* 5: 29–36

Fadiman J (1965) *Behavior change following psychedelic (LSD) therapy*. Dissertation, Stanford University, 1965 (download from www.proquest.com)

Fadiman J (2011) *The psychedelic explorers guide: Safe, therapeutic, and sacred journeys*. Rochester, VT: Park Street Press
Fadiman J (2016a) Microdose research. *Psychedelic Press* 15: 53–59

Fadiman J (2016b) Statement, quoted in: Gregoire (2016)

Fadiman (2017) Statement, quoted in: Waldman (2017). 108–109

Fadiman J, Korb S (2018a) Webinar, presented by The Psychedelic Society of Toronto, Canada. January 2018. https://www.youtube.com/watch?v=cmfW25doED4&t=145s

Fadiman J (2018b) Email to Robert Forte. Quoted in Forte R (2018) Email to Torsten Passie, 01-18-2018

Fadiman J (2018c) Emails to Torsten Passie, July-September 2018

Family N, Vinson D, Vigliocco G, Kaelen M, Bolstridge M, Nutt DJ, Carhart-Harris RL (2016) Semantic activation in LSD: evidence from picture naming. *Language, Cognition and Neuroscience*, DOI: 10.1080/23273798.2016.1217030

Fanciullacci M, Franchi G, Sicuteri F (1974) Hyperreactivity to lysergic acid diethylamide (LSD-25) and psilocybin in essential headache. *Experientia* 30: 1441–1443

Finnis DG, Kaptchuk TJ, Miller F, Benedetti F (2010) Biological, clinical, and ethical advances of placebo effects. *Lancet* 375: 686–695

Fischer R, Fox R (1972) Creative performance and the hallucinogenic drug-induced creative experience. *J of Psychedelic Drugs* 5: 29–36

Forrer GR, Goldner RD (1951) Experimental physiological studies with lysergic acid diethylamide (LSD-25). *Arch Neurol* (Am.) 65: 581–588

Forte R (ed.) (1997) *Entheogens and the future of religion*. San Francisco, CA: Council on Spiritual Practices

Forte R (ed.) (1999) *Timothy Leary: Outside looking in*. Rochester, VT: Park Street Press

Forte R (2018) Email to Torsten Passie, 01-18-2018

Frederking W (1955) Intoxicant drugs (mescaline and lysergic acid diethylamide) in psychotherapy. *J Nerv Ment Dis* 121: 262–266

Frederking W (1953/54) Über die Verwendung von Rauschdrogen (Meskalin und Lysergsäurediäthlamid) in der Psychotherapie. *Psyche* 7: 342–364

Freedman DX, Appel JB, Hartman FR, Molliver ME (1964) Tolerance to behavioral effects of LSD-25 in the rat. *J Pharmacol Exp Therap* 143: 309–313

Freedman DX, Coquet CA (1965) Regional and subcellular distribution of LSD and effects on 5-HT levels. *Pharmacologist* 7: 183

Garcia S (2016) Microdosing: I spent 14 days using LSD to increase productivity … kind of. February26, 2016, available at https://thehustle.co/how-to-lsd-microdose, accessed 25-12-2017

Gasser P, Kirchner K, Passie T (2015) LSD-assisted psychotherapy for anxiety associated with a life-threatening disease: a qualitative study of acute and sustained subjective effects. *J Psychopharmacol.* 29: 57–68

Gastaut H, Ferrer S, Catsells C, Lesevre N, Luschnat K (1953) Action de la diethylamide de l'acide d-lysergique (LSD-25) sur les functions psychiques et l'electroencephalogramme. *Confin Neurol* 13: 102–20

Geert-Jørgensen E (1961) Modelpsykoser og Lysergsyre-Diethyl amidbehandling. Ugeskrift for *Laeger* 123: 1452–1455

Ghose T (2015) Short trip? More people 'microdosing' on psychedelic drugs. Available at: https://www.livescience.com/51482-more-people-microdosing-psychedelic-drugs.html, accessed 26-01-2018

Gnirss F (1965): Neurosentherapie mit psycholytischen Stoffen. In: Kielholz P (ed.) *Psychiatrische Pharmakotherapie in Klinik und Praxis.* Bern, Stuttgart: Huber. 135–151

Gottlieb A (1997) *Peyote and other psychoactive cacti.* Berkeley, CA: Ronin

Gordon PE (1975) *The effects of LSD on the expression of affect in psychotherapy.* New York University Ph.D. Dissertation

Gouzoulis-Mayfrank E, Schreckenberger M, Sabri O, Arning C, Thelen B, Spitzer M, Kovar K A, Hermle L, Bull U, Sass H (1999) Neurometabolic effects of psilocybin, 3,4-methylenedioxyethylamphetamine (MDE) and d-methamphetamine in healthy volunteers. A double-blind, placebo-controlled PET study with [18F]-FDG. *Neuropsychopharmacol* 20: 565–581

Graham JR (1967) Cardiac and pulmonary fibrosis during methysergide therapy for headache. *Amer J Med Sci* 254: 1–12

Gregoire C (2016) Everything you wanted to know about microdosing (but were afraid to ask). January 13, 2016, avalable at https://www.huffingtonpost.com/author/carolyn-gregoire, accessed 12-12-2017

Greiner T, Burch NR, Edelberg R (1957) Threshold doses of LSD in human subjects. *Fed Proc* 16: 303

Greiner T, Burch NR, Edelberg R (1958) Psychopathology and psychophysiology of minimal LSD-25 dosage: A preliminary dosage-response spectrum. A.M.A. *Arch Neurol Psychiat* 79: 208–210

Gresch PJ, Smith RL, Barrett RJ, Sanders-Bush E. Behavioral tolerance to lysergic acid diethylamide is associated with reduced serotonin-2A receptor signaling in rat cortex. *Neuropsychopharmacol* 30: 1693–1702

Grim R (2004) Who's got the acid? These days, almost nobody. Available at http://www.slate.com/articles/news_and_politics/hey_wait_a_minute/2004/04/whos_got_the_acid.html

Grob Plante S (2017) Meet the world's first online LSD microdosing Ccach. September 7, 2017. Available at https://www.rollingstone.com/culture/features/meet-the-worlds-first-online-lsd-microdosing-coach-w499104, accessed 01-01-2018

Grof S (1980) The effects of LSD on chromosomes, genetic mutation, fetal development and malignancy. In: Grof S. *LSD psychotherapy*. Pomona, CA: Hunter House. 320–347

Grof S, Dytrych Z (1965) Blocking of LSD reaction by premedication with Niamid. *Activ Nerv Sup* 7: 306

Halpern JH, Pope HG (2003) Hallucinogen persisting perception disorder: what do we know after 50 years? *Drug Alcohol Depend* 69: 109–119

Halpern JH, Lerner AG, Passie T (2018) A review of Hallucinogen Persisting Perception Disorder (HPPD) and an exploratory study of subjects claiming symptoms of HPPD. *Curr Top Behav Neurosci* 36: 333–360

Harman W, Fadiman J (1970) Selective enhancement of specific capacities through psychedelic training. In: Aaronson B, Osmond H (eds.) *Psychedelics: The uses and implications of Hallucinogenic Drugs*. Garden City, NY: Anchor Books. 239–257

Harman WW, McKim RH, Mogar RE, Fadiman J, Stolaroff MJ (1966) Psychedelic agents in creative problem- solving: a pilot study. *Psychol Rep* 19: 211–227

Hartmann RP (1974) *Malerei aus den Bereichen des Unbewussten*. Köln: Dumont

Hasler F, Bourquin D, Brenneisen R, Bär T, Vollenweider FX (1997) Determination of psilocin and 4-hydroxyindole-3-acetic acid in plasma by HPLC-ECD and pharmacokinetic profiles of oral and intravenous psilocybin in man. *Pharm Acta Helv* 72: 175–184

Heard G (1965) A poignant poet. *The Kenyon Review* 27: 49–79

Heard G (1959) *Training for a life of growth*. Santa Monica, CA: The Wayfarer Press

HeatlessBBO (2017) LSD microgram dosage effects (self LSD). Available at https://www.reddit.com/r/LSD/comments/5uvk68/lsd_microgram_dosage_effects/

Henderson LA, Glass WJ (eds.) (1994) *LSD: Still with us after all these years*. New York: Lexington Books

Hermle L, Funfgeld M, Oepen G, Botsch H, Borchardt D, Gouzoulis E, Fehrenbach RA, Spitzer M (1992) Mescaline-induced psychopathological, neuropsychological, and neurometabolic effects in normal subjects: Experimental psychosis as a tool for psychiatric research. *Biol Psychiatry* 32: 976–91

Hewitt MP (960) Discussion. In: Abramson HA (ed.) *The use of LSD in psychotherapy*. New York: Josiah Macy. 61

Hintzen A, Passie T (2010) *The pharmacology of LSD*. Oxford, London, New York et al.: Oxford University Press

Hirsch MW, Jarvik ME, Abramson HA (1956) Lysergic Acid Diethylamide (LSD-25): XVIII. Effects of LSD-25 and Six Related Drugs upon Handwriting. *J Psychol* 41: 11–22

Hoch PH (1956) Studies in routes of administration and counteracting drugs. In: Cholden L (ed.) *Lysergic Acid Diethylamide and Mescaline in Experimental Psychiatry*. New York: Grune & Stratton, 8–12

Hoch P, Cattell JP (1952) Effects of Mescaline and lysergic acid (d-LSD-25). *Am J Psychiatry* 108: 579–584

Hoffer A (1960) Discussion. In: Abramson HA (ed.) *The use of LSD in psychotherapy*. New York: Josiah Macy Jr. Foundation. 41

Hoffer A, Osmond H (1966) *New hope for alcoholics*. New York: University Books

Hoffer A, Osmond H (1967) *Hallucinogens*. New York, London: Academic Press

Hofmann A, Horowitz M (1976) Interview with Albert Hofmann. *High Times* 11, July 1976: 25–28, 31, 81

Hogle LF (2005) Enhancement technologies and the body. *Annual Rev Anthropology* 34: 695–716

Holland D, Passie T (2011) *Flashback-Phänomene als Nachwirkung von Halluzinogeneinnahme*. Berlin: VWB

Hollister LE (1961) Clinical, biochemical and psychologic effects of psilocybin. *Arch Int Pharmacodyn Ther* 130: 42–52

Hollister L (1968) *Chemical psychoses*. Springfield, ILL: C.C. Thomas

Horgan J, Halpern JHH (2017) The promise of LSD microdoses and other psychedelic "medicines". Available at https://blogs.scientificamerican.com/cross-check/the-promise-of-lsd-microdoses-and-other-psychedelic-medicines/, accessed 01-01-2018

Horsley RR, Palenicek T, Kolin J, Vales K (2018) Psilocin and ketamine microdosing: effects of subchronic intermittent microdoses in the elevated plus-maze in male Wistar rats. *Behav Pharmac* 2018 Mar 13. doi: 10.1097/FBP.0000000000000394

Idanpään-Heikkilä JE, Schoolar JC (1969) 14C-lysergide in early pregnancy. *Lancet* 2: 221

International Crops Research Institute for the Semi-Arid Tropics (2011) Fertilizer Microdosing on Degraded Soils in Sub-Saharan Africa. Available at https://farmingfirst.org/2011/01/fertilizer-microdosing-on-degraded-soils-in-sub-saharan-africa/, accessed 07-07-2018

International Crops Research Institute for the Semi-Arid Tropics (2009) Fertilizer microdosing. Boosting production in unproductive land. Available at http://www.icrisat.org/impacts/impact-stories/icrisat-is-fertilizer-microdosing.pdf, accessed 07-07-2018

Isbell H, Fraser HF, Wikler A, Belleville RE (1955) Tolerance to diethylamide of lysergic acid (LSD-25). *Fed Proc* 14: 354

Isbell H, Belleville RE, Fraser HF, Wikler A, Logan CR (1956) Studies on lysergic acid diethylamide (LSD-25): I. effects in former morphine addicts and development of tolerance during chronic chronic intoxication. *AMA Arch Neurol Psychiatr* 76: 468–78

Isbell H, Jasinski DR (1969) A comparison of LSD-25 with (-)-delta-trans-tetrahydrocannabinol (THC) and attempted cross-tolerance between LSD and THC. *Psychopharmacologia* 14: 115–123

Isbell H, Logan C (1957) Studies on the diethylamide of lysergic acid (LSD-25). *AMA Arch Neurol Psychiatr* 77: 350–358

Isbell H, Wolbach AB, Wikler A, Miner EJ (1961) Cross tolerance between LSD and psilocybin. *Psychopharmacologia* 2: 147–159

Jarvik ME, Abramson HA, Hirsch MW (1955a) Lysergic acid diethylamide (LSD-25): IV. Effect on attention and Concentration. *J Psychol* 39: 373–383

Jarvik ME, Abramson HA, Hirsch MW (1955b) Lysergic acid diethylamide (LSD-25): VI. Effect upon recall and recognition of various stimuli. *J Psychol* 39: 443–454

Jarvik ME, Abramson HA, Hirsch MW, Ewald AT (1955c) Lysergic acid diethylamide (LSD25): VIII. Effect on arithmetic test performance. *J Psychol* 39: 465–473

Jay M (2018) The world's first-ever acid trip actually kinda sucked. Available at https://www.vice.com/en_us/article/8xpmzb/the-worlds-first-ever-acid-trip-actually-kinda-sucked, accessed 12-05-2018

Jdyf333 (2017) ?(from the 1980s) LSD product insert. Available at https://www.flickr.com/photos/jdyf333/2075297284/, accessed 03-03-2018

Johnstad PG (2018) Powerful substances in tiny amounts: An interview study of psychedelic microdosing. *Nordic Studies on Alcohol and Drugs* 35: 39–51

Jonas S, Downer JC (1964) Gross behavioural changes in monkeys following administration of LSD-25, and development of tolerance to LSD-25. *Psychopharmacologia* 6: 303–306

Karst M, Halpern JH, Bernatek M, Passie T (2010) The non-hallucinogen 2-bromo-lysergic acid diethylamide as preventative treatment for cluster headache: an open, non-randomized case series. Cephalalgia 30: 1140–1144

Kast EC, Collins VJ (1964) Study of lysergic acid diethylamide as an analgesic agent. *Anesth Analg* 43: 285–291

Kauder E (1899) Ueber Alkaloide aus Anhalonium Lewinii. *Archiv der Pharmazie* 237: 190–198

Ketchum J (2006) *Chemical warfare secrets almost forgotten.* Santa Rosa, CA: Chembooks

Khazan O (2017) Tiny amounts of LSD for depression. *The Atlantic Daily*, January 14, 2017. Available at https://www.theatlantic.com/health/archive/2017/01/ayelet-lsd-microdosing/513035/, accessed 11-20-2017

Khazan O (2017) Tiny amounts of LSD for depression, January 14, 2017. Available at https://www.theatlantic.com/health/archive/2017/01/ayelet-lsd-microdosing/513035/, accessed 03-03-2018

Kihlbohm M, Netz B (1967) [LSD-25: An introductory survey]. *Lakartidningen* 64: 1842–1855

Kirsch I, Deacon BJ, Huedo-Medina TB, Scoboria A, Moore TJ, Johnson BT (2008) Initial severity and antidepressant benefits: A meta-analysis of data submitted to the Food and Drug Administration. *PLOS Medicine* 5, e45. doi: 10.1371/journal.pmed.0050045

Klee GD, Bertino J, Weintraub W, Callaway E (1961) The influence of varying dosage on the ffects of lysergic acid diethylamide (LSD-25) in humans. *J Nerv Ment Dis* 132: 404–409

Klock JC, Boerner U, Becker CE (1974) Coma, hyperthermia and bleeding associated with massive LSD overdose. *West J Med* 120: 183–188

Korngold M (1963) LSD and the creative process. *Psychoanalytic Review* 50: 152–155

Korb S (2018a) Microdosing psychedelics: what's all the fuss about? Lecture at *"Beyond Psychedelics"* conference, Prague June 22, 2018

Korb S (2018b) Email to Torsten Passie, August 6, 2018

Kornetsky C, Humphries O (1957) Relationship between effects of a number of centrally acting drugs and personality. *AMA Arch Neurol Psychiatr* 77: 325–327

Kornetsky C, Humphries O, Evarts EV (1957) Comparison of psychological effects of certain centrally acting drugs in man. *AMA Arch Neurol Psychiatr* 77: 318–324

Kraehenmann R, Pokorny D, Aicher H, Preller KH, Pokorny T, Bosch OG, Seifritz E, Vollenweider FX. LSD Increases primary process thinking via serotonin 2A receptor activation. *Front Pharmacol.* 2017 Nov 8;8:814. doi: 10.3389/fphar.2017.00814. eCollection 2017

Kreppel G (1964) *Die psychischen Phänomene im Schwellenbereich des Meskalin.* Bonn: Friedrich-Wilhelms-Universität Dissertation

Krippner S (1969) The psychedelic state, the hypnotic trance, and the creative act. In: Tart CT (ed.) *Altered states of consciousness.* New York: John Wiley & Sons. 271–290

Krippner S (1985) Psychedelic drugs and creativity. *J Psychoactive Drugs* 17: 235–246

Krippner S (1983) A short interview with Dr Stanley Krippner. *The Psychozoic Press* 6: 46–54

Kumar N (2016) *Microdosing: Enhance you vitality, temperament and efficiency with hallucinogenic.* Poland: Amazon Books on Demand

Kurland AA, Savage C, Pahnke W, Grof S, Olsson J (1971) LSD in the treatment of alcoholics. *Pharmakopsychiatrie/Neuropsychopharmakologie* 4: 83–94

Kuromaro S, Okada S, Hanada M, Kasahara Y, Sakamoto K (1967) The effects of LSD on the phantom limb phenomenon. *Lancet* 87: 22–27

Kuypers K (2018) Email to Torsten Passie, February 17, 2018

Kuypers K et al. (2018) LSD microdosing – a dose finding study [trial synopsis], available at http://www.trialregister.nl/trialreg/admin/rctview.asp?TC=7102 accessed 07-07-2018

Kvale S, Brinkmann S (2015) InterViews: Learning the craft of qualitative research interviewing. Los Angeles, CA: Sage

Lanz U, Cerletti A, Rothlin E (1955) Distribution of lysergic acid diethylamide in the organism. *Helv Physiol Pharmacol Acta* 13: 207–16

Lappin G (2015) The expanding utility of microdosing. *Clin Pharmacol Drug Dev* 4: 401–406

Lappin G, Kuhnz W, Jochemsen R, Kneer J, Chaudhary A, Oosterhuis B, Drijfhout WJ, Rowland M, Garner RC (2006) Use of microdosing to predict pharmacokinetics at the therapeutic dose: experience with 5 drugs. *Clin Pharmacol Ther* 80: 203–215

Lee MA, Shlain B (1985/1994) *Acid dreams: The complete social history of LSD*. New York: Grove Press

Lennard H, Jarvik ME, Abramson HA (1956) Lysergic acid diethylamide (LSD-25): XII. A preliminary statement of its effects upon interpersonal communication. *J Psychol* 41: 185–198

Leonard A (2015) How LSD Microdosing Became the Hot New Business Trip. Availabe at https://www.rollingstone.com/culture/features/how-lsd-microdosing-became-the-hot-new-business-trip-20151120, accessed 25-01-2018

Levine A, Abramson HA, Kaufman MR, Markham S (1955a) Lysergic acid diethylamide (LSD-25): XVI. The effect on intellectual functioning as measured by the Wechsler-Bellevue Intelligence Scale. *J Psychol* 40: 385–395

Levine A, Abramson HA, Kaufman MR, Markham S, Kornetsky C (1955b) Lysergic acid diethylamide (LSD-25): XVI. Effect on personality as observed in psychological tests. *J Psychol* 40: 351–366

Leuner H (1958) Seelische Abbildungsvorgänge als Phänomene der Psychodynamik. In: Winkler WT, Kretschmer W (ed.) *Mehrdimensionale Diagnostik und Therapie*. Stuttgart: Thieme. 178–187

Leuner H (1959) Psychotherapie in Modellpsychosen. In: Speer, (ed.) *Kritische Psychotherapie*. München: J.F. Lehmanns 1959. 94–102

Leuner H (1962) *Die experimentelle Psychose*. Berlin, Göttingen, Heidelberg: Springer

Leuner H (1971) Halluzinogene in der Psychotherapie. *Pharmakopsychiatrie / Neuropsychopharmakologie* 4: 333–351

Leuner H (1981) *Halluzinogene*. Bern, Stuttgart, Wien: Huber

Leuner H (1994) Personal communication.

Leuner H, Schönfelder H (1981) Simulation der beginnenden Schizophrenie durch unterschwellige Halluzinogendosis und der Einfluß sozialer Bedingungen. In: Leuenr H. *Halluzinogene*. Bern, Stuttgart, Wien: Huber. 129–153

Levine A, Abramson HA, Kaufman MR, Markham S, Kornetsky C (1955) Lysergic acid diethylamide (LSD-25): XVI. Effect on personality as observed in psychological tests. *J Psychol* 40: 351–366

Levine A, Abramson HA, Kaufman MR, Markham S (1955) Lysergic acid diethylamide (LSD-25): XVI. The effect on intellectual functioning as measured by the Wechseler-Bellevue Intelligence Scale. *J Psychol* 40: 385–95

Liddel DW, Weil-Malherbe H (1953) The effects of methedrine and of lysergic acid diethylamide on mental processes and on the blood adrenaline levels. *J Neurosurg Psychiat* 16: 7–13

Liebert RS, Werner H, Wapner S (1958) Studies in the effect of lysergic acid diethylamide (LSD-25): self- and object-size perception in schizophrenics and normal adults. *AMA Arch Neurol Psychiatr* 79: 580–584

Liechti M (2018) Personal communication, August 2018

Liechti ME, Dolder PC, Schmid Y (2017) Alterations of consciousness and mystical-type experiences after acute LSD in humans. *Psychopharmacology* (Berl) 234: 1499–1510

Lienert GA (1964) *Belastung und Regression*. Meisenheim/Glahn: Anton Hain

Lienert GA (1959) Changes in the factor structure of intelligence tests produced by d-lysergic acid diethylamide (LSD). In: Bradley PB (ed.) *Neuropsychopharmacology*. Amsterdam: Elsevier. 461–463

Liechti M, (2017) Modern clinical research on LSD. *Neuropsychopharmacology* 2017: 1–14

Liggenstorfer R (2018) Email to Torsten Passie, January 2018

Ling TM, Buckman J (1963) *Lysergic acid diethylamide (LSD-25) & Ritalin in the treatment of neuroses*. London: Lambarde Press

Linton HB, Langs RJ, Paul IH (1964) Retrospective alterations on the LSD experience. *J Nerv Ment Dis* 138: 409–23

Luft F (2017) *Microdosing LSD*. Poland: Amazon Books on Demand

Maclay WS, Gutmann E (1941) Mescaline hallucinations in artists. *Arch Neurol Psychiat* 41: 130–137

MacLean KA, Johnson MW, Griffiths RR (2011) Mystical experiences occasioned by the hallucinogen psilocybin lead to increases in the personality domain of openness. *J Psychopharmacol* 25: 1453–1461

Malitz S (1960) Discussion. In: Abramson HA (ed.) *The use of LSD in psychotherapy.* New York: Josiah Macy Jr. Foundation. 53

Malleson N (1971): Acute adverse reactions to LSD in clinical and experimental use in the United Kingdom. *Brit J Psychiatry* 118: 229–30

Maloof M. (2016) Statement, quoted in: Cruz RW (2016) *Microdosing LSD.* New York: Open Book Publishing

Marazzi A (1954) *First psychochemical conference*, May 12, 1954 Edgewood Artsenal [conference report]. Available at http://www.dtic.mil/dtic/tr/fulltext/u2/077032.pdf, accessed 03-03-2018

Marecek P, Bakalar E, Zeman K (1968) Attempt of blocking LSD intoxication with tranylcypromine. *Activitas Nervosa Superior* 10: 276–277

Marona-Lewicka D, Kurrasch-Orbaugh DM, Selken JR, Cumbay MG, Lisnicchia JG, Nichols DE (2002) Re-evaluation of lisuride pharmacology: 5-HT1a receptor-mediated behavioral effects overlap its other properties in rats. *Psychopharmacol* 164: 93–107

Marona-Lewicka D, Nichols CD, Nichols DE (2011) An animal model of schizophrenia based on chronic LSD adminstration: old ideas, new results. *Neuropharmacology* 61: 503–512

Marona-Lewicka D, Thisted RA, Nichols DE (2011) Distinct temporal phases in the behavioral pharmacology of LSD: dopamine D2 receptor-mediated effects in the rat and implications for psychosis. *Psychopharmacology* 180: 427–435

Marshall C (1937) An inquiry into the causes of mescal visions. *Journal of Neurology and Psychopathology* 17: 289–304

Martin DA, Marona-Lewicka D, Nichols DE, Nichols CD (2014) Chronic LSD alters gene expression profiles in the mPFC rlevant to schizophrnia. *Neuropharmacology* 83: 1–8

Masters REL, Houston J (1968) *Psychedelic Art.* New York: Grove Press

Matrixblogger (2017) Gehirn auf LSD: Mikrodosierung Abschlussbericht. 27. Oktober 2017, available at https://www.matrixblogger.de/gehirn-auf-lsd-mikrodosierung-abschlussbericht-biohacker-teil-8/, accessed 25-12-2017

Matsumoto J, Jouvet M (1964) Effects of reserpine, DOPA and 5-HTP on the 2 sleep states. *Comp Rend Soc Biol* 158: 2137–2140

Mayer-Gross W, McAdam W, Walker J (1952) Lysergsäure-Diäthylamid und Kohlenhydratstoffwechsel. *Nervenarzt* 23: 30–31

Mayer-Gross W, McAdam W, Walker J (1951) Psychological and biochemical effects of lysergic acid diethylamide. *Nature* 168: 827

McDonough J (1985) *San Francisco ROCK*. San Francisco, CA: Chronicle Books

McGlothlin WH, Cohen S, McGlothlin MS (1967) Long lasting effects of LSD on normals. *Arch General Psychiat* 17: 521–532

McKenna T (1992) *Food of the Gods*. New York: Bantam

Middendorf W (2001) Personal communication.

Moncrieff J (2008) *The Myth of the Chemical Cure*. Basingstoke, Hampshire UK: Palgrave Macmillan

Mongeau B (1974) The effect of Hydergine on cerebral blood flow in diffuse cerebral insufficiency. *Eur J Clin Pharmacol* 7: 169–75

Moreno FA, Wiegand CB, Taitano EK, Delgado PL (2006) Safety, tolerability, and efficacy of psilocybin in 9 patients with obsessive-compulsive disorder. *J Clin Psychiatry* 67: 1735–1740

Mueller F, Lenz C, Dolder PC, Harder S, Schmid Y, Lang UE, Liechti ME, Borgwardt S (2017) Acute effects of LSD on amygdala activity during processing of fearful stimuli in healthy subjects. *Transl Psychiatry* 7: e1084

Mueller F, Lenz C, Dolder P, Lang U, Schmidt A, Liechti M, Borgwardt S (2017) Increased thalamic resting-state connectivity as a core driver of LSD-induced hallucinations. *Acta Psychiatr Scand* 136: 648–657

Mueller F, , Dolder P, Schmidt A, Liechti M, Borgwardt S (2018) Altered network hub connectivity after acute LSD administration. *Neuroimage* 18: 694–701

Muzio JN, Roffwarg HP, Kaufman E (1966) Alterations in the nocturnal sleep cycle resulting from LSD. *Elecroenceph Clin Neurophysiol* 21: 313–24

Nebigil CG, Hickel P, Messaddeq N, Vonesch JL, Douchet MP, Monassier L, György K, Matz R, Andriantsitohaina R, Manivet P, Launay JM, Maroteaux L (2001) Ablation of serotonin 5-HT(2B) receptros in mice leads to abnormal cardiac structure and function. *Circulation* 103: 2973–2979

Nichols DE (2016). Psychedelics. *Pharmacol Rev* 68: 264–355

Nichols D (2017) Microdosing with LSD and its research potential. Available at http://heffter.org/microdosing-lsd-research-potential/, accessed 03-09-2017

Nichols D (2018) Mail to Torsten Passie, September 18, 2018

Nichols DE, Grob CS (2018) Is LSD toxic? *Forensic Science International* 284: 141–145

Nichols D, Roseman L, Timmermann C (2018) Psychedelics: From pharmacology to phenomenology. An interview with David Nichols. *ALIUS Bulletin* 2: 75–85

Novak SJ (1997) LSD before Leary: Sidney Cohen's critique of 1950s psychedelic drug research. *Isis* 88: 87–110

Osa (2014) Mikrodosing von Psychedelika als Nootropika. November 21, 2014 available at https://eve-rave.ch/Forum/viewtopic.php?t=38618, accessed 25-12-2017

Oswald I (1965) Some psychophysiological features of human sleep. *Progr Brain Res* 18: 160–169

Pahnke WN, McGothlin W (1967) Discussion. In: Abramson HA (ed.) *The use of LSD in psychotherapy and alcoholism.* Indianapolis, New York, Kansas City: Bobbs Merrill. 40–41

Papac DI, Foltz RL (1990) Measurement of lysergic acid diethylamide (LSD) in human plasma by gaschromatography/negative ion chemical ionization mass spectrometry. *J Anal Toxicol* 14: 189–190

Partridge BJ, Bell SK, Lucke JC, Yeates S, Hall WD (2011) Smart drugs "as common as coffee": Media hype about neuroenhancement. *PLoS ONE*, 6(11), e28416. doi:10.1371/journal. pone.0028416

Passie T (1996/1997) Hanscarl Leuner: Pioneer of hallucinogen research and psycholytic therapy. *Bulletin of the Multidisciplinary Association for Psychedelic Studies* 7 (1): 46–49, available at https://www.maps.org/news-letters/v07n1/07146leu.html

Passie T (1997) *Psycholytic and psychedelic therapy research 1931–1996: a complete international bibliography.* Hannover: Laurentius Publishers

Passie T (2005) The use of psilocybin in psychotherapy. In: Metzner R (ed.) *Sacred Mushroom of Visions: Teonanácatl.* Rochester, VM: Park Street Press. 113–138

Passie T, Benzenhöfer U (2018) MDA, MDMA, and other "mescaline-like" substances in the US military's search for a truth drug (1940s to 1960s). *Drug Test Anal* 10: 72–80

Passie T, Seifert J, Schneider U, Emrich HM (2002) The pharmacology of psilocybin. *Addict Biol* 7: 357–364

Passie T, Halpern JH, Stichtenoth DO, Emrich HM, Hintzen A (2008) The pharmacology of lysergic acid diethylamide: a review. *CNS Neuroscience and Therapeutics* 14: 295–314

Passie T, Halpern JH (2014) The pharmacology of hallucinogens. In: Ries R, Fiellin D, Miller S, Saitz R, Gorelick DA (eds.) *Principles of addiction medicine*. 5th edition. Philadelphia et al.: Wolter Kluwer 2014. 235–255

Pathak S (2017) The upside of LSD: This guy wants you to microdose on psychedelics. September 5, 2017, available at http://www.ozy.com/rising-stars/the-upside-of-lsd-this-guy-wants-you-to-microdose-on-psychedelics/80018, accessed 25-12-2017

Peel HW, Boynton AL (1980) Analysis of LSD in urine using radioimmunoassay - Excretion and storage effects. *Can Soc Forensic Sci J* 13: 23–28

Pierce J (1961) Zur Wirkung von Atarax auf die LSD-Modellpsychose. *Praxis* 50: 486–91

Pletscher A, Ladewig D (eds.) (1994) *50 years of LSD: Current status and perspectives of hallucinogens*. New York: Parthenon

Preller KH, Herdener M, Pokorny T, Planzer A, Kraehenmann R, Stämpfli P, Liechti ME, Seifritz E, Vollenweider FX (2017) The fabric of meaning and subjective effects in LSD-induced states depend on serotonin 2A receptor activation. *Curr Biol* 27: 451–457

Presti D (2017) Statement, quoted in: Waldman (2017). 108

Primac DW, Mirsky AF, Rosvold HE (1957) Effects of centrally active drugs on two tests of brain damage. AMA Arch Neurol Psychiatr 77: 328–332

Prochazkova L, Lippelt DP, Colzato LS, Kuchar M, Sjoerds Z, Hommel B (2018) Exploring the effect of microdosing psychedelics on creativity in an open-label natural setting. *Psychopharmacology* 235: 3401-3413

Rascon FI, Paredes A (2015) *Tarahumara Medicine: Ethnobotany and Healing among the Rarámuri of Mexico*. Norman, OK: University of Oklahoma Press

Repantis D, Schlattmann P, Laisney O, Heuser I (2010) Modafinil and methylphenidate for neuroenhancement in healthy individuals: A systematic review. *Pharmacological Research* 62187–206

Resnick O, Krus DM, Raskin M (1964) LSD-25 action in normal subjects treated with a monoamine oxidase inhibitor. *Life Sci* 35: 1207–1214

Riba J, Romero S, Grasa E, Mena E, Carrio I, Barbanoj MJ (2006) Increased frontal and paralimbic activation following ayahuasca, the pan-Amazonian inebriant. *Psychopharmacology* 186: 93–8

Richards, L, Milton J, Spratto GR (1969) *LSD-25: A Factual Account.* Washington DC: US Dept. of Justice, Bureau of Narcotics and Dangerous Drugs. 1

Rickli A, Moning OD, Hoener MC, Liechti ME (2016) Receptor interaction profiles of novel psychoactive tryptamines compared with classic hallucinogens. *Eur Neuropsychopharmacol.* 26: 1327–1337

Robinson JT, Chitham RG, Greenwood RM, Taylor JW (1974) Chromosome aberrations and LSD. *Br J Psychiatry* 125: 238–244

Rogers C (1959) Toward a theory of creativity. In: Anderson H (ed.) *Creativity and its Cultivation.* New York: Harper. 69–82

Roseman B (1963) *225,000 Indians can't be wrong.* Joshua Tree, CA: Self-published

Roseman B (1966) *LSD: The age of mind.* N. Hollywood, CA: Wilshire Book Co.

Roth BL (2007) Drugs and valvular heart disease. *New England Journal of Medicine* 356: 6–9

Roubicek (1962) Therapeutic effect of lysergic acid diethylamide (LSD). *Act Nerv Sup* 4: 240–241

Rucker JJH, Iliff J, Nutt D (2017) Psychiatry & the psychedelic drugs. Past, present & future. *Neuropharmacology,* https://doi.org/10.1016/j.neuropharm.2017.12.040

Rushkoff D (2017) Statement, quoted in: Zweifel P (2016)

Safer DJ (1970) The effect of LSD on sleep-deprived men. *Psychopharmacology* 17: 414–424

Salerno EV, Tallaferro A (1956) Mescalina, acido lisergico y function menstrual. *Boletin Sociedad Obstetrica Ginecologica* (Buenos Aires) 35: 269–275

SAMSHA (2016) available at https://www.samhsa.gov/data/all-reports, accessed 09-09-2018

Sandison RA (1954) Psychological aspects of the LSD treatment of the neuroses. *J Ment Sci* 100: 508–515

Sandison RA (1960) Discussion. In: Abramson HA (ed.) *The use of LSD in psychotherapy.* New York: Josiah Macy, 44

Sandison, RA, Spencer AM (1954) The Therapeutic Value of Lysergic Acid Diethylamide in Mental Illness. *Journal of Mental Science* 100: 491–507

SANDOZ (1951) Prospectus for the use of LSD in clincical practice. Reprinted in: Hofmann A. *LSD my problem child.* Sarasota, FL: MAPS

Sankar DVS (1975) Reversibility, tolerance, and cross reactions. In: Sankar DVS (ed.) *LSD: A total study.* Westbury, NY: PJD Publications. 565–574

Sankar DVS, Sankar DB, Phipps E, Gold E (1961) Effect of administration of Lysergic acid diethylamide on serotonin levels in the body. *Nature* 191: 499–500

Sankar DVS, Cates NR, Domjan M (1969) Comparative biochemical pharmacology of psychoactive drugs. *Clin Res* 17: 395

Sapiensoup (2017) Microdosing LSD: Smart drug or placebo? Available at https://sapiensoup.com/microdosing-lsd, accessed 12-12-2017

Savage C (1952) Lysergic acid diethylamide: A clinical-psychological study. *Amer J Psychiat* 108: 896–900.

Savage C (1955) Variations in ego feeling induced by d-lysergic acid diethylamide (LSD-25). *The Psychoanalytic Review* 42: 1–16

Schindler EA, Gottschalk CH, Weil MJ, Shapiro RE, Wright DA, Sewell RA (2015) Indoleamine Hallucinogens in Cluster Headache: results of the cluster busters medication use survey. *J Psychoactive Drugs* 47: 372–381

Schmid Y, Enzler F, Gasser P, Grouzmann E, Preller KH, Vollenweider FX (2015) Acute effects of lysergic acid diethylamide in healthy subjects. *Biol Psychiatry* 78: 544–553

Schönfelder H (1967) Über niedrig dosierte experimentelle Psychosen und ihre Beziehung zur beginnenden Schizophrenie. Göttingen: Georg-August-University, Medical Dissertation

Schwarz BE, Bickford Rg, Mulder DW, Rome HP (1956) Mescaline and LSD-25 in activation of temporal lobe epilepsy. *Neurology* 6: 275–280

Sercl M, Kovarik J, Jaros O (1961) Klinische Erfahrungen mit Psilocybin (CY 39 Sandoz). *Psychiatria et Neurologia* 142: 137–146

Sessa B (2017) *The Psychedelic Renaissance.* 2d ed. New York: SUNY

Sewell RA, Halpern JH, Pope HG Jr (2006) Response of cluster headache to psilocybin and LSD. *Neurology* 66, 1920–1922

Sheflin AW, Opton EM (1978) *The mind manipulators*. New York: Paddington Press

Sicuteri F (1963) Prophylaktische Behandlung der Migräne mit Lysergsäurederivaten. *Triangel* 6 (3): 116–123

Sicuteri F (1977) Headache as metonymy of non organic central pain. In: Sicuteri F (ed.) *Headache: New Vistas*. Florence: Biomedical Press. 19–67

Silva MTA, Carlini EA, Claussen, U, Korte F (1968). Lack of cross-tolerance in rats among delta-trans-tetrahydrocannabinol. Cannabis extract, mescaline and LSD. *Psychopharmacologia* 13: 332–340

Sloane B, Doust JWL (1954) Psychophysical investigations in experimental psychoses: results of the exhibition of D-lysergic acid diethylamide to psychaitric patients. *J Mental Sci* 100: 129–144

Smart RG, Bateman K (1968) The chromosomal and teratogenic effects of lysergic acid diethylamide: A review of the current literature. *Can Med Assoc J* 99: 805–810

Snyder SH, Reivich M (1966) Regional localization of LSD in monkey brain. *Nature* 209: 1093–1095

Sokoloff L, Perlin S, Kornetsky C, Kety SS (1957) The effects of d-lysergic acid diethylamide on cerebral circulation and overall metabolism. *Ann NY Acad Sci* 66: 468–477

Solon O (2016) Would you take LSD to give you a boost at work? WIRED takes a trip inside the world of microdosing. Wired UK. Available at http://www.wired.co.uk/article/ lsd-microdosing-drugs-silicon-valley, accessed 07-07-2018

Soskin RA (1973) Short-term psychotherapy with LSD: A case study. *J Religion and Health* 12: 41–62

Speck LB (1957) Toxicity and effects of increasing doses of mescaline. *J Pharmacol Exp Ther* 119: 78–84

Spitzer M, Thimm M, Hermle L, Holzmann P, Kovar KA, Heimann H, Gouzoulis-Mayfrank E, Kischka U, Schneider F (1996) Increased activation of indirect semantic associations under psilocybin. *Biol Psychatry* 39: 1055–1057

Stafford P, Golightly B (1967) *LSD: The problem-solving psychedelic*. New York: Award Books

Stafford P, Golightly B (1969) *LSD in Action*. London: Sidgwick & Jackson

Stolaroff M (1994) *Thanatos to Eros: 35 years of psychedelic exploration*. Berlin: VWB

Stolaroff M (1999) Are psychedelics useful in the practice of Buddhism? *J Hum Psychology* 39: 60–80

Stoll WA (1947) Lysergsäure-diäthylamid, ein Phantastikum aus der Mutterkorngruppe. *Schweizer Arch Neurol Psychiat* 60: 279–323

Stoll A, Rothlin E, Rutschmann J, Schalch WR (1955) Distribution and fate of 14C-labeled lysergic acid diethylamide (LSD 25) in the animal body. *Experientia* 11: 396–397

Strajhar P, Schmid Y, Liakoni E, Dolder PC, Rentsch KM, Kratschmar DV et al (2016) Acute effects of lysergic acid diethylamide on circulating steroid levels in healthy subjects. *J Neuroendocrinol* 28: 12374

Strassman RJ, Qualls CR, Uhlenhuth EH, Kellner R (1994) Dose-response study of N,N-dimethyltryptamine in humans: II. subjective effects and preliminary results of a new rating scale. *Arch Gen Psychiat* 51: 98–108

Tagliazucchi E, Roseman L, Kaelen M, Orban C, Muthukumaraswamy SD, Murphy K, Laufs H, Leech R, McGonigle J, Crossley N, Bullmore E, Williams T, Bolstridge M, Feilding A, Nutt DJ, Carhart-Harris R (2016) Increased global functional connectivity correlates with LSD-induced ego dissolution. *Curr Biol* 26: 1043–1050

Tande MI, Fliflet F (2017, September 27) LSD inntar lesesalene: Det er en «moodlifter» i stu- diehverdagen [LSD enters the reading rooms: – It is a mood lifter for study days]. Universitas. Retrieved from http://universitas.no/kultur/ 62876/lsd-inntar-lesesalene-det-er-en-moodlifter-I, accessed 07-07-2018

Techlos (2014) [Internet entry on microdosing with mescaline]. Available at https://www.reddit.com/r/microdosing/comments/2nle72/tarahumara_indians_microdosing_peyote/, accessed 19-12-2017

Tewari T, Mukherjee S (2010) Microdosing: Concept, application and relevance. *Perspect Clin Res* 1: 61–63

Tijo JH, Pahnke WN, Kurland AA (1969) LSD and chromosomes. *JAMA* 210: 849–856

Tonini G, Montanari C (1955) Effects of experimentally-induced psychoses on artistic expression. *Conferences of Neurology* 15: 225–239

Torda C (1968) Contribution to serotonin theory of dreaming (LSD infusion). *NY State J Med* 68: 1135–1138

Tovihoudji PG, Irenikatché Akponikpè PB, Agbossou EK, Bertin P, Bielders CL (2017) Fertilizer microdosing enhances maize yields but may exacerbate nutrient mining in maize cropping systems in northern Benin. *Field Crops Research* 213: 130–142

Toyoda J (1964) The effects of chlorpromazine and imipramine on the human noctural sleep electroencephalogram. *Folia Psychiat Neurol Jap* 18: 198–211

Trout K (2005) *Trout's notes on san pedro & related trichocerus species.* Better Days Publishing

Trout K (2018) Mail to Torsten Passie, 01-21-2018

Ulrich RF, Patten BM (1991) The rise, decline and fall of LSD. *Perspect Biol Med* 34: 561–78

Ungerleider JT, Fisher DD (1967) The problems of LSD-25 and emotional disorder. *California Medicine* 106: 49–55

Upshall DG, Wailling DG (1972) The determination of LSD in human plasma following oral administration. *Clin Chim Act* 36: 67–73

Van Dusen W (1961) LSD and the enlightment of Zen. *Psychologica* 4: 11–16

Vojtěchovský M, Safratová V, Havránková O (1972) Effect of threshold doses of LSD on social interaction in healthy students. *Act Nerv Sup* 14: 115-6

Vollenweider FX, Kometer M (2010) The neurobiology of psychedelic drugs: implications for the treatment of mood disorders. *Nature Reviews Neuroscience* 11: 642–651

Vollenweider FX, Leenders KL, Scharfetter C, Maguire P, Stadelmann O, Angst J (1997) Positron emission tomography and fluorodeoxyglucose studies of metabolic hyperfrontality and psychopathology in the psilocybin model of psychosis. *Neuropsychopharmacol* 16: 357–72

Vollenweider FX, Vollenweider-Scherpenhuyzen MF, Babler A, Vogel H, Hell D (1998) Psilocybin induces schizophrenia-like psychosis in humans via a serotonin-2 agonist action. *Neuroreport* 9: 3897–3902

Wacker D, Wang S, McCorvy LD, Betz RM, Venkatakrishnan AJ, Schools Z, Dror RO, Nichols DE, Roth BL (2017) Crystal structure of an LSD bound human serotonin receptor. *Cell* 168: 377–389

Wade K (1994) LSD and Depression. *Psychedelic Illuminations* 7: 44–46
Waldman A (2017) *A Really Good Day: How microdosing made a mega difference in my mood, my marriage and my life.* New York: Alfred A. Knopf

Weidmann H, Taeschler M, Konzett H (1958) Die Pharmakologie von Psilocybin. *Experientia* 14: 378–379

Weyl B (1951) *Versuch einer psychopathologischen Analyse der LSD-Wirkung.* Freiburg im Breisgau: Albert-Ludwig-University Freiburg, Medical dissertation

Winter JC (1971) Tolerance to a behavioral effect of lysergic acid diethylamide and cross-tolerance to mescaline in the rat: Absence of a metabolic component. *J Pharmacol Exp Ther* 178: 625–630

Winter JC, Eckler JR, Rabin RA (2004) Serotonergic/glutamatergic interactions: The effects of mGlu2/3 receptor ligands in rats trained with LSD and PCP as discriminative stimuli. *Psychopharmacology* 172: 233–240

Woods B (2016) Can very small doses of LSD make you a better worker? I decided to try it. March 2, 2016, availabe at https://www.vox.com/2016/3/2/11115974/lsd-internet-addiction, accessed 25-12-2017

Yanakieva S, Polychroni N, Family N, Williams LTJ, Luke DP, Terhune DB (2018) The effects of microdose LSD on time perception: a randomised, double-blind, placebo-controlled trial. Psychopharmacology 2018 Nov 26. doi: 10.1007/s00213-018-5119-x

Zareva T, Harris S (2017) Can psychedelics help you expand your mind? August 17, 2017, available at http://bigthink.com/design-for-good/lsd-is-regaining-popularity-through-the-practice-of-microdosing-and-attracting-scientific-interest, accessed 01-01-2018

Zegans LS, Pollard JC, Brown D (1967) The Effects of LSD-25 on Creativity and Tolerance to Regression. *Arch Gen Psychiat* 16: 740–749

Zweifel P (2016) Noch eine Dosis LSD vor dem Meeting. Süddeutsche Zeitung, December 1, 2016, available at http://www.sueddeutsche.de/karriere/job-noch-eine-dosis-lsd-vor-dem-meeting-1.3274964

Printed in Great
Britain
by Amazon